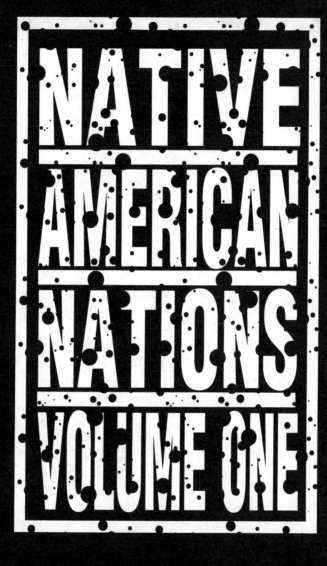

NATIVE AMERICAN NATIONS VOLUME ONE

CREDITS

Writing
Nigel D. Findley

Development
Tom Dowd
Vegas Assistance
Richard Jordan

Editorial Staff
Senior Editor
Donna Ippolito
Assistant Editor
Sharon Turner Mulvihill

Production Staff
Art Director
Dana Knutson
Cover Art
Larry Elmore
Cover Design
Joel Biske
Book Design
Jeff Laubenstein
Illustration
Janet Aulisio
Tim Bradstreet
Rick Harris
Jeff Laubenstein
Larry MacDougall
Jim Nelson
Layout
Tara Gallagher

Published by
FASA Corporation
P.O. Box 6930
Chicago, IL 60680

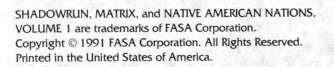

CONTENTS

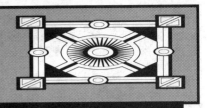

PEACE-KEEPER

PEACEKEEPER: A Prologue

As our traditions tell us, we have come together to speak and to listen, to share and to receive wisdom, to give what we can to our brother nations, and draw from them the support we need. The voice was full, rich with power that rang through even the poor quality of the recording. The words had a singsong cadence that made the listeners think of a ritual invoked many times, or a ceremony losing its deeper meaning with the passing years. *Let us speak and listen, and open our hearts one to another.*

Two figures sat in the dark room and listened to the recorded voice. Their body language spoke of a common purpose and mutual respect, but not of friendship.

The older of the two—a rail-thin man with eyes of cold steel and sleek black hair pulled back severely into a ponytail—reached out and stabbed PAUSE with a long finger. "That is…?"

The woman, as smoothly muscular as he was whipcord slender, answered him in a flat voice. "Wilson Gold Eagle, First Speaker of the Sovereign Tribal Council. Head honcho of the Native American Nations."

The man nodded and struck PLAY. The recorded voice continued in the same singsong style, meaningless ritual opening what might be a meaningless meeting.

From the corner of her eye, the woman watched the man. The light was low in the room, but her Zeiss optics picked out the details. He wore a black leather vest, dusty with age, over an open-necked gray shirt. Tight black jeans were tucked into rattlesnake-skin boots. (Real skin? The woman wondered. Funding might not be a problem after all…) He glinted with silver: toe caps on his boots, his belt buckle, a plain band around his right wrist, and a finely linked chain that tied back his ponytail. No weapons visible, but the feather, leather, and wood fetishes adorning his belt and peeking from the pockets of his vest told her that he might not need the mundane implements on which she depended. Her eyes were drawn to his right hand as it rested on the arm of the chair. The first two fingers were moving rhythmically. She noticed, slightly shocked, that his long, razor-sharp fingernails—natural, not cyber chrome—were tearing gouges in the synthleather of the upholstery.

"Who is that?"

The man's question forced her attention back to the recording.

A second man was speaking. His voice contrasted sharply with the first voice: still powerful, it was the power of a heavy club rather than that of a smooth-flowing river.

"That's Paul Shaggy Mountain," she replied after a moment. "Chief of the Cascade Ork. He's troll."

"I know what he is," the man said impatiently. He hit PAUSE again. "Aurora. Is there anything of interest in the recording? Is it worth my time to listen to it?"

The woman hesitated. "I listened to the whole thing," she answered slowly, "and I think it's just drek—useless maundering, petty political maneuvering, those fragging tribals talking about their traditions." Her voice dripped with contempt.

"Wipe it, then."

"What?" Aurora sat forward. "You wanted the slotting recording. You said it was important." Her voice became more accusatory. "You don't have any idea how tricky it was getting a recorder into that session, particularly since you said it couldn't be implanted, it had to be carried."

The man laughed, an ironic, chilling sound. His laugh made the woman shiver involuntarily. "Everything I said was true," the man said. "It was important. It is just that the recording itself is of no value."

Aurora inhaled sharply. "You wanted to see if it was possible to smuggle something into the Council meeting."

"And your man proved it was."

"What are you planning, Jesse?"

Jesse laughed again. "You know what I am planning. Shatter the Council and bring down the so-called tribal nations. You have no need to know the details…yet."

"The policlub committee won't back you."

Jesse spat on the carpeted floor. Once again the woman was shocked and disturbed. "Puling weaklings," he snapped. "All talk, no vision."

"I think they may try to block you."

"Let them." Jesse leaned back and locked his slender fingers behind his head. "The blind leaders and their blind rank and file. Let them try. I spit on the Humanis Policlub." He turned a winning, warm smile on the tense woman. "Except, of course, for you and your people. The true heart; the ones with vision, the ones who are willing to act. Let the others fall into line when the deed is done, when they see what we have accomplished." His voice became softer, almost musical, but the hard edge of determination, or fanaticism, perhaps, still shone in his cold eyes. "You will be the leaders, I the guide. Together we will complete what others have dreamed of and lack the guts to even attempt. The destruction of the tribal nations."

Aurora was silent, tense, as she considered the question she had to ask. "Your background," she said slowly, "is tribal."

She'd expected a burst of anger, even violence; she was surprised by his laughter. "Yes, my background is tribal. But I renounce it, I repudiate it. I am not tribal. I revile my parents, my upbringing, the traditions with which they tried to bind me." He toyed with a bone-and-feather fetish on his belt. "I use some of their skills, but only the more easily to destroy them."

"What are you going to smuggle into the Council chamber?"

"Something special," he answered. "Something I…acquired…from the good people at Renraku. Oh, the corporators are useful from time to time."

"A bomb?"

A grim, secretive smile twisted Jesse's face. "In a way.

Something that will blow the NAN apart. Something—" He stopped abruptly and his gaze snapped toward the door. "What was that?"

"I didn't hear—"

"Shut up." He motioned for silence. His eyes closed and his breathing slowed.

Fear thrilled up and down the woman's spine as she realized the man was assensing. Reflexively, razor-sharp spurs snapped into place, protruding from the woman's left arm. Her right hand rested on the butt of her Colt Manhunter.

Jesse's eyes snapped open, and he flowed to his feet with one graceful motion. "We have company," he said softly. "In the hall. Four. Renraku security guards." He grinned, a mirthless baring of teeth. "I suppose they hope to take their property back."

Aurora was on her feet too. "We can leave the back way," she said. "We—"

He gestured her to silence again. "I do not run from such as them," he said coldly. His gaze bored into the apartment door. One hand toyed with a fetish.

A sound came from the hallway, a click of metal on metal. One of the corporate soldiers was clumsy.

Jesse muttered something under his breath. The woman felt her scalp crawl as she saw the man's face begin to change. His nose and mouth seemed to extend slightly, becoming a narrow snout; his eyes contracted, took on a red tinge. He pointed with a finger—now more like a claw—at the center of the door. He hissed a single, sharp syllable.

The door exploded into the hall as though struck by a bullet-train. The heavy laminate shattered as it struck the first two security guards with monstrous force. Fragments of door tore into their broken bodies.

The corporators were well-trained. The other two spun into the doorway, one high and one low, their Ares Crusader machine pistols leveled and spitting death. Aurora dived for cover, feeling the pounding impact as the light rounds flattened against her body armor. Prone behind the couch, she brought her heavy pistol to bear. She spared a quick glance for Jesse, expecting to see the hollow-point bullets tearing his unarmored body into bloody shreds.

But he stood there unharmed, a deadly smile on his face. In the darkness of the room, she saw his body limned with a shimmering glow that reminded her of heat lightning. The corp-cops cut loose again, this time concentrating their fire on the black-clad man. Ricochets whined through the room, shattering the playback unit and stitching the walls, as the rounds bounced off Jesse's arcane armor.

Aurora squeezed off a single, perfectly aimed shot. The heavy slug tore through one soldier's face-screen just above the nose. The body flipped backward out the door, its helmet—torn off by the impact—bouncing down the hallway. She tracked the barrel over to the single surviving corp-cop, who was frantically trying to jam another clip into his machine pistol. Her finger tightened on the reactive trigger.

"No!" Jesse's voice was a whiplash. "He's mine." He smiled like death at the doomed corp-cop. "Sorry, chummer," he murmured. Then another phrase of power hissed through his clenched teeth.

The corp-cop screeched in agony, the despairing cry turning to a burble and then to silence. The woman looked down at the pool of red-gray sludge, all that remained of the Renraku soldier.

Jesse sighed, as relaxed as she'd ever seen him. "I think we should move on, don't you?" He reached a hand down to the woman to help her to her feet. She shied away from his touch; fear and disgust warred in her expression. He straightened again. "As you will."

He turned his back on her and stepped over the corpses into the hallway. Her eyes stayed on him as he strode away from the killing zone.

INTRODUCTION

Native American Nations, Volume 1 is a roleplaying adventure and sourcebook set in the world of **Shadowrun**. The year is 2052. Advances in technology are astonishing, with humans able to merge with computers and travel through that netherworld of data known as the Matrix. Even more astonishing is the return of magic to the world. Elves, dragons, dwarfs, orks, and trolls have assumed their true forms, while megacorporations (rather than superpowers) rule much of the world. North America has been balkanized into sovereign states, many tribal in nature and occupied only by Native Americans ("Amerindians"). Moving through it all like whispers in the night are the shadowrunners. No one admits their existence, but no one else can do their secret work.

Native American Nations includes a complete roleplaying scenario, **Peacekeeper**, that leads the players on a merry chase through tribal lands. In addition to being an entertaining adventure, this scenario will show the gamemaster how the quirks of a culture can be used to add excitement and intrigue to a gaming session.

The sourcebook section provides the gamemaster with background information on four of the eight Native American nations, members of the NAN Sovereign Tribal Council. Each of the eight native nations is a unique society and culture, with its own eccentricities, strengths, and weaknesses. Each has its own world view, its own place in the grand scheme of things, its own direction…and its own problems for those who run the shadows. **Native American Nations** gives gamemasters the detailed background information they need to run adventures in diverse tribal societies, and to make these nations come alive for the players.

GAMEMASTERING NOTES

The adventure, **Peacekeeper**, is linear, structured around a prolonged pursuit. (In this way, it is similar to "road movies" like *Midnight Run*.) During the adventure, the runners pursue a toxic shaman named Jesse John and attempt to foil his nefarious schemes.

Jesse's plan, as detailed in this adventure, makes sense…to Jesse. But almost by definition, a toxic shaman's mind has been twisted, so the logic of his route may escape others.

To run the adventure, the gamemaster needs a thorough familiarity with the contents of this book as well as a working knowledge of the basic **Shadowrun** rules. The contents of the adventure section of this book are for the gamemaster's eyes only, except for certain items earmarked as handouts for the players. (It is okay for the players to read the sections on the different Amerindian nations; presumably, they would have access to this information by scanning the local Shadowland™ bulletin board.) Everything needed to roleplay **Peacekeeper** is included here.

Peacekeeper is designed for a party of four to eight player characters. The group should contain a variety of talent, including at least one shaman and one decker. Combat skills will be very important to a successful run.

Some encounters in this adventure are thoroughly planned out and described in detail. Others merely set the scene and remain open-ended. Hints for gamemastering the various sections are included with each section.

The gamemaster may make any and all changes deemed necessary to adapt **Peacekeeper** to a particular group of players and characters.

MAKING SUCCESS TESTS

During the course of the adventure, the players will make a number of Unresisted Success Tests using a skill and a given Target Number. These Unresisted Success Tests will be indicated by the name of the appropriate skill and the Target Number. For example, a Stealth (4) Test would mean an Unresisted Stealth Success Test with a Target Number of 4.

SUCCESS TABLES

At times, the gamemaster will use Success Tables to determine how much information the players receive. Each Success Table lists different information for different numbers of die roll successes. Unless otherwise noted, the player should receive all the information for the level of success he rolled, as well as all the information for lower levels of success. For example, a character achieving 3 successes would receive the information for 3 successes as well as the information for 1 and 2 successes.

All animals have a natural Unarmed Combat skill equal to their Reaction.

HOW TO USE THIS BOOK

Aside from the basic **Shadowrun** rules, this book includes everything needed to play this adventure. It is recommended, however, that the gamemaster also be familiar with certain aspects of **The Grimoire**, specifically the **Toxic Shaman** and **Spirits** sections.

The gamemaster should read through the entire adventure before beginning the game. Some important plot developments will not become apparent until well into the adventure, but the gamemaster will have to lay the groundwork much earlier on. He can only do that by being familiar with the storyline.

The gamemaster should also examine the maps, plans, and diagrams found throughout **Peacekeeper**, especially the floor plans of the various buildings. He will also want to read through the appendix sections relating to the tribal nations involved (Ute, Pueblo, and Salish-Shidhe) to become familiar with the atmosphere and "texture" of each nation. This will prove important when roleplaying inhabitants and officials of the nation in question.

The **Plot Synopsis** is a summary of the story background and the course the adventure was designed to follow.

Peacekeeper begins with the section **Two for the Show**, which offers suggestions on how to get the ball rolling and draw the players into the adventure. The adventure follows, and is divided into short sections describing each of the encounters the players will face, or are likely to face, in the course of roleplaying **Peacekeeper**.

Most of the encounters begin with a section called **Tell It To Them Straight**. This should be read verbatim to the shadowrunners and describes where they are and what is happening to them as though they were actually there. The gamemaster may find that he occasionally needs to adapt the text to special circumstances or the actions of the shadowrunners. Any special instructions to the gamemaster are printed in **boldface** type.

Next is the information section, **Behind the Scenes**. This is the real story, for only the gamemaster knows what is really going on at any given moment in an adventure. If there is a map needed to play this encounter, it is included in this section. Non-player character stats needed to roleplay the section are usually included here as well, though in some cases the gamemaster may be directed to existing Archetype or Contact game statistics in the **Shadowrun** (SR) rulebook or the **Sprawl Sites** (SS) sourcebook.

Finally, each section includes hints under **Debugging**. These notes include suggestions for getting the story back on track if things go too far wrong. This section also suggests how to deal with characters who get discouraged and how to prevent the characters from getting killed off too easily. The gamemaster is, of course, always free to ignore these hints and let the chips fall where they may.

Legwork contains the information the player characters can obtain through their Contacts or through the public data nets.

Cast of Shadows includes major non-player-character descriptions and stats.

Picking Up the Pieces includes tips on awarding Karma, and contains newsnet items to be used as handouts for the players, depending on the outcome of the adventure.

PLOT SYNOPSIS

Jesse John was born an Amerindian and raised on Hecate Strait in the Queen Charlotte Islands in the days before Tsimshian seceded from NAN. His parents did their best to inculcate Jesse with respect and appreciation for his heritage, but Jesse was a troubled youth. He rebelled against the native teachings and his upbringing.

It appeared that Jesse would also rebel against basic human decency. When he was fourteen, he killed a man for no apparent reason. His parents tried to shelter him from the consequences, but the elders of the tribe were determined to discipline the youth in the old way.

Jesse took off before he could experience these old ways first-hand. He ran away from home and built a new life for himself in Seattle. Despite his native origin, Jesse John cherished a rabid hatred for the tribal culture and way of life; not just his own tribe, but all tribes. His outspoken vehemence earned him notice from various factions and, despite his appearance and background, Jesse was invited to join the Humanis Policlub.

Surrounded by people who shared his hate, Jesse grew increasingly violent in his actions and attitudes, and more and more unstable. Two years ago he stepped over the fine line separating sanity and madness.

Jesse continues to violently reject his tribal heritage and all NAN stands for, but has taken advantage of the power available through shamanism. Jesse John is a shaman, but he has chosen a destructive totem: he is a Toxic shaman.

Some of his fellow policlub members began to worry about Jesse, and their concern increased when he came to them and said he had a simple plan to blow apart the NAN and destroy its influence once and for all. He would not divulge the details, but the Humanis members know that Jesse's plan cannot help but be cunning, twisted, probably bloodthirsty, and potentially quite effective.

This plan has caused a split in the policlub membership. Jesse's claims disturbed the cooler heads among the Humanis (yes, cool heads do belong to the policlub). The young members, borderline psychos, and hotheads believe that Jesse is onto something. (This situation echoes the historic split between the Irish Republican Army, who recognized that offing Prime Minister Maggie Thatcher would not be a particularly good PR coup for the cause, and the Provisional IRA (the "Provos"), who thought that toasting Maggie would be more fun than St. Pat's day. Even the somewhat loony-tune Provos split when their hotheads, the INLA, thought it would be wiz to bomb a couple of NATO radar installations.)

Officially, the Humanis Policlub has cut Jesse John loose. Some of their lunatic-fringe members still support him. They think his idea of blowing the NAN apart is a good one, and they will back him with everything they have.

This is where the shadowrunners come in. They are approached by Mr. Johnson, ostensibly an Aztechnology suit, and asked to track down one Mr. Jesse John. Once they find him, they proceed as they see fit. If they feel confident that they can bring him in in one piece, do it. If even the slightest doubt exists, the order is "beyond salvage, terminate with extreme prejudice." As the runners can learn if they try, Mr. Johnson is actually Karl Brackhaven, a senior member of the Humanis Policlub's Central Seattle chapter.

Jesse's plan is a simple concept with a potentially difficult execution. Using his undeniable intelligence and his considerable shamanic powers, Jesse intends to stir up serious trouble in several of the major North American Amerindian nations. The nature of the trouble will vary from nation to nation, but local investigators in each nation will draw only one possible conclusion: the "trouble" was caused by agents of one or more of the other Amerindian nations. Jesse plans to go even further with the Salish-Shidhe Council. He will make sure that all the Council tribes are at each other's throats. If he does it right, and there is no reason to think that he is going to blow it, Sioux will be against Pueblo, Ute will be against Sioux, Cascade Ork will be against just about everyone. Not quite the Apocalypse, but pretty fragging close.

The runners pick up Jesse's trail when he is on his way to detonate his first political bombshell in Las Vegas, Ute Nation. He plans to sucker the runners into entering the Pueblo Council's sophisticated corner of the Matrix, the "Net." He has already planted evidence linking this illegal penetration to the Sioux Special Forces so that when the runners get themselves geeked, Pueblo will blame Sioux for trying to jack around with their computer resources, and will also be none too happy with Ute.

The next stop is Pueblo in Pueblo Council. Jesse has contacted a small group of orks, members of an underground Awakened tribe, and set up a BTL deal, pretending to be a representative of the Sioux intelligence system. Jesse has also "programmed" a particularly twisted troll named Crunch to believe that he will be part of an important operation. In fact, Jesse has set Crunch up. One of Jesse's associates will assassinate a high-profile Pueblo politician and leave Crunch's (already dead) body behind. The "assassin," conveniently killed by security forces, will be loaded with evidence incriminating the Sioux Special Forces.

Finally, Jesse will go to Seattle, where he plans to break up a meeting of the Salish-Shidhe Council. He will smuggle an emotion-manipulating device, a tonal generator, into the Grand Council Lodge. Under the influence of the generator, the Council members, who are already going to be discussing very sensitive topics, will be driven to fits of anger that should break up the meeting—and potentially the entire Salish-Shidhe Council structure.

Of course, Jesse is not alone in his crusade. He is assisted by a cybered woman named Aurora and a number of other hotheads and firebrands from among the Humanis Policlub. Unfortunately for someone, the runners are not the only people on Jesse's trail. The shaman managed to acquire his tonal generator from Renraku, and the megacorporation wants it back. Several squads of Renraku soldiers are tracking Jesse, and they will not be making much distinction between the runners and Jesse's own followers. Finally, an elite team of FBI agents has followed Jesse from Seattle, with instructions to stop him at any cost. These federal agents have learned that the runners are in the employ of Karl Brackhaven and conclude, understandably, that they are part of the support team for Jesse's mission.

The team is out there alone, and must stop Jesse to save NAN.

TWO FOR THE SHOW

TELL IT TO THEM STRAIGHT

You walk into the dark tavern and your subconscious antennae pick up the undercurrent of danger. Death lurks in the shadows, and the air seems to vibrate with barely repressed violence. You scan the Blue Flame Tavern. All but one of the cramped booths along the side wall are filled with nightmarish shapes; hulking figures, hard and angular, highlighted here and there by the glint of metal. All eyes are upon you. Some are glowing, some reflect the washed-out neon of the beer sign over the bar. Your sensitive hearing picks up an almost-subliminal hiss as a mentally controlled metal spur slips out of its flesh sheath.

You smile. The good ol' Blue Flame hasn't changed at all.

"Hoi, chummers," the barkeep greets you in his thin, strongly-accented voice. A good-natured grin shows his lack of teeth. "Heard about the score you pulled last week. Good work, smooth moves. First round on the house, ha?" Without waiting for an answer, he starts pouring drinks, your usuals.

Your grin broadens. When the Chinaman passes out free drinks, it means he's either going to shortchange you later in the evening or water your booze. Nothing ever changes at the Blue Flame.

You've taken your regular booth and the free drinks are a warm glow in your bellies when the Chinaman appears at your table. "Company looking for you earlier, ha?" he says. "Bobsie Twins. Said they be back later. Maybe soon. You want to use back door?"

You hesitate, thinking about it. As far as you know, there's no heat out for you—and you're starting to feel the pinch again. The money from your last score is gone and it's time to look for more work.

The Chinaman takes your silence as his answer. "Your call," he mumbles, heading back to his haven behind the bar. "Your funeral."

You've hardly made a dent in your second round of drinks (yep, watered) when the "Bobsie Twins" make their appearance. They're big men with close-cropped hair. Both have been around, but that's where the outward similarity ends. But you can see why the Chinaman referred to them as "twins." Despite the differences in appearance, they feel the same, they have the same aura. They give off the signals that all sararimen from the same corporation have, that indefinable aura of sameness that overlays their superficial differences. (Is that it? Are the Bobsie Twins undercover corporate muscle?)

Bobsie One janders over to your table and stops a safe half-meter away. Bobsie Two stands close-cover, a meter back, a meter to One's right (perfect overlapping arcs of fire for two right-handers; the Twins know their stuff).

"My boss got a proposition for you," Bobsie One announces in a voice that sounds like twenty klicks of bad road. "You want a job, you follow us. Got it?"

BEHIND THE SCENES

The "Bobsie Twins" are members of the Humanis Policlub. Not too bright, they are the perfect "personal expediters" for Karl Brackhaven, president of the Humanis Central Seattle chapter. Their mission is simply to bring the runners to a meet with Brackhaven at the lounge in the Ritz Hotel at Fourth and Blanchard downtown. They are not expected to like this job, and they don't. They will be as disrespectful and supercilious as they can without putting the runners off the meet entirely. This attitude is especially obvious if there are any metahumans or Amerindians among the party.

The Bobsie Twins refuse to divulge any information about their boss. They do not know what mission he has in mind for the runners. They have also been told that if they fail to get the runners to appear for the meet, they will be in deep drek. Thus, the two razorguys are forced to walk a fine line between blowing the meet and being polite to people they consider little better than animals.

Once the runners have agreed to the meet, the Bobsie Twins leave the tavern, jump aboard their Harley hogs and cruise downtown toward the Ritz. The runners must provide their own transportation, but the Bobsie Twins will make sure they are not far behind.

BOBSIE TWINS

Two chromed born losers, the "Bobsie Twins" have just about enough brains between them to know which way to shoot in a firefight. They are physically tough, though, and loyal to the employer who provides them with raw meat, booze, women, and the occasional elf to geek. They are perfect "blunt instruments," and thus useful to their employer, Karl Brackhaven. Quite different in appearance, the Bobsie Twins might otherwise have come out of the same mold.

B	Q	S	C	I	W	E	M	R	Armor
6(8)	3(5)	6(8)	1	1	3	0	—	2(5)	None

Dice Pools: Defense (Armed) 4, Defense (Unarmed) 6, Dodge 5
Skills: Armed Combat 4, Bike 2, Etiquette (Street) 2, Firearms 4, Stealth 2, Unarmed Combat 6
Cyberware: Cybereyes (w/flare compensation), Dermal Plating (2), Muscle Replacement (2), Retractable Spurs, Smartgun Link, Wired Reflexes (2)
Gear: Ingram Smartgun [32 (clip), 5M3, with silencer], Harley Scorpion, Survival Knife (8L3)

CONDITION MONITOR						
		MENTAL				
		PHYSICAL				
L		M		S		D/UNC

CONDITION MONITOR						
		MENTAL				
		PHYSICAL				
L		M		S		D/UNC

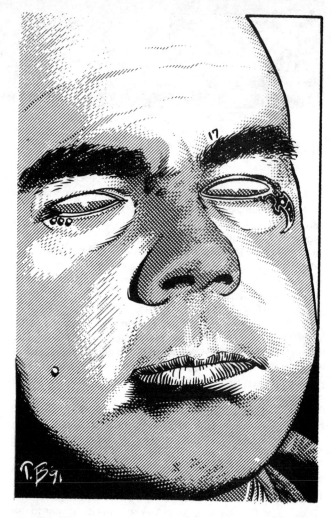

DEBUGGING

Nothing would please the Bobsie Twins more than to slot with the runners, but they have a job to do. If it looks like they have pushed things too far, the razorguys will back off from their obnoxious approach and be (almost) civil to the runners. If pressed, Bobsie One will hand over a credstick bearing a balance of 2,000¥ as a "token of my boss' earnest…whatever that means."

The runners may refuse the Bobsie Twins' invitation, or even get into a scrap with them. If the runners refuse, the razorguys will be forced to return to their boss and report failure; if the runners fight, the razorguys will give it their all.

In either case, the runners will receive a second invitation to a meet at the Ritz through another channel, perhaps a familiar fixer. This invitation will include an apology for "sending animals to do a man's work."

The invitation will be extended a second time if the runners reject the first offer. After that, the runners are out of this adventure and will hear through their street contacts several months later that another group of runners saved the nation from war. (A vastly overstated version of events, but not too good for the runners' tender egos).

When the runners accept the invitation, go to **Putting on the Ritz,** the next section.

PUTTING ON THE RITZ

TELL IT TO THEM STRAIGHT

Read the following to the players when their characters arrive.

The current Ritz Hotel is the third incarnation of an establishment that first appeared on the Seattle scene in the early 20th century. Initially, it was a haven of Old World charm and sophistication. But toward the end of the century, old-style hostelries fell on hard times, losing their business to flashy, modern establishments catering to business clients who had no time to appreciate old-fashioned hospitality. The old Ritz closed down. Its name was picked up by a flophouse that opened on the "bad" end of Denny Way. When the flophouse burned down in 2040, the name was available again and the New Ritz was born. It quickly gained a reputation as a haven for high-level corporate execs.

Actually, the name "New Ritz" is in some ways a misnomer. The new hotel, though equipped with the cutting edge of labor-saving technology, leans toward the old definition of comfort and luxury. The rooms are sumptuous, the staff well-trained and polite, the service impeccable. And the lounge—you've heard it described as an oasis of civilization in the cultural wasteland of downtown Seattle. You're looking forward to your visit.

As you try to enter the tastefully appointed foyer, an impeccably suited maître d' steps from an alcove and politely bars your way.

"Good evening, and welcome to the Ritz," he intones in a European accent that is almost real. "You are expected, of course. But I must ask you to check your weapons. A Ritz tradition, you understand, as much for your own protection and peace of mind as for our other guests'."

Read the following to the players when their characters enter the restaurant.

As you enter, one of the patrons looks up and smiles at you with a corporator's perfect teeth. He looks in his early 40s, and could easily have just stepped off the cover of an average megacorp's annual report. Conservative suit, his tie in this season's power color—bright turquoise—with an ear-stud to match, his only other jewelry is a wristwatch worth about as much as a small yacht. Handsome son-of-a-slitch, you think, just oozing bonhomie. (You find yourself recalling a pre-Chaos adage: "Sincerity's the key; once you can fake that, you're in.") He beckons you over and indicates the chairs around his table.

"Good evening," he begins as you seat yourselves. "I'm Mr....Johnson.

"My...associates...and I have need of your services. We are negotiating with certain parties within the Native American Nations and would like to see our transaction concluded smoothly and with no interruptions. We've learned, through various sources, that some of our competitors have joined forces to try

and stop us. Their operative has instructions to do whatever is necessary to block our deal. *Whatever is necessary.* We know the operative, and we know his track record. He's an expert, and he doesn't care who gets hurt as long as he completes his assignment. It is no exaggeration to say that he would not hesitate to start a war to meet his contract."

The corporator lays a dossier on the table in front of you. "This is the operative, one Jesse John. Shaman, assassin, provocateur. He is insane, but that doesn't keep him from being deadly effective.

"This is your assignment. We want you to stop Jesse. Capture him and bring him back to us alive if you can. If you can't," he shrugs, "your instructions are 'beyond salvage, terminate with extreme prejudice.' Do I make myself clear?

"Obviously, my associates and I would prefer to deal with this matter ourselves rather than involving outsiders. Handling matters in-house, however, would compromise our source. We are not willing to do that.

"When you have Jesse, or proof that he is no longer a threat, leave a message at the front desk of the Ritz. I will contact you."

Mr. Johnson taps the dossier with a manicured finger. "Our assets inform us that Jesse John is currently bound for Las Vegas. He is traveling under the name of Ben Johnson." The corporator smiles frostily. "No relation." Then he's all business again. "His travel information is in the dossier. I hope you see fit to begin the pursuit immediately."

BEHIND THE SCENES

The human maître d' is actually a Street Mage (fighter orientation), and he will not tolerate any trouble. He will refuse to admit the runners until and unless they turn over to him for safekeeping all of their (obvious) weapons. The maître d's alcove is actually a sophisticated electronics scanner. The gamemaster should make a 7-dice Perception Test against the Concealability of any weapon the players are carrying to determine whether the sensors pick it up. If the scanners detect the weapon, the maître d' will politely ask the runner to check the weapon before entering the lounge, naming the weapon and its location specifically. Characters who refuse will be invited to wait in the foyer while the rest of the party enters the lounge.

Aggressive action is not tolerated in the New Ritz. Arguing with the maître d' will get the player characters a warning, then personal attention from the Ritz's security team. (The security team uses the archetypes listed.) The security team normally consists of five Corporate Security Guards (Partial Heavy Armor, Stun Batons, Tasers, and Uzi IIIs, **SR**, p. 165), a Company Man (**SR**, p. 164), and two Wage Mages (**SR**, p. 38). The team will arrive within one minute of any disturbance. The security team will enter the hotel lobby from various directions and will seek to neutralize and expel, rather than kill, their opponents.

If the runners are willing to surrender their (obvious) weapons, they may enter the lounge.

The Ritz lounge has the ambience of an Edwardian gentlemen's club: thick Afghan rugs on hardwood floors, small tables of dark oak, wingback chairs upholstered in burgundy leather, walls lined with bookcases, and—serious anachronism!—what looks for all the world like a working fireplace. The tech is there, but hidden. Each table has a white-noise generator (Rating 7), and the entire room is protected by a Rating 6 ward. The room is almost empty (with the prices here, the lounge needs only a few patrons to turn a profit).

Karl Brackhaven set the meet here for two reasons. The first is to convince the runners that he is, in fact, a corporator of power and prestige. The second is that the Ritz is a "controllable" venue. Through the lavish distribution of nuyen, Brackhaven can ensure that no one "remembers" the runners' presence and that the maître d's electronic log has no record that they were ever there. (Such are the "guest services" at the Ritz.)

Since the moment the Bobsie Twins first approached the runners, Brackhaven has had the team under observation. His eventual salary offer will depend on how the runners handled themselves. For example, if they followed the razorguys without question, he will decrease the offer (the runners are stupid), if they yakked about their destination to anyone else, he will also decrease the offer (the runners have big mouths), and so on.

THE DEAL

Karl Brackhaven has gone to great lengths to create his corporate exec persona. His dress, manner of speech, and the venue he chose for the meet all fit. He has also bribed the maître d' 1,000¥ to record that "Mr. Johnson's" bill was charged to an Aztechnology expense account. His watch is an expensive model with the Aztechnology corporate logo worked subtly into the pattern on the face; it takes a Perception/Intelligence (5) Test to notice this. This final piece of evidence is so subtle that it should go a long way toward reassuring the runners that Mr. Johnson is actually the corporator he pretends to be. They will have doubts, but only those normal for dealing with the unknown.

Brackhaven is offering 115,000¥ as payment for the "neutralization" of Jesse John. The runners can decide among themselves how to split the money. As a gesture of good faith, Brackhaven will present a credstick with a balance of 20,000¥. The rest of the money is payable on delivery of Jesse—alive or dead—or irrefutable proof of his death. (Brackhaven is counting on the reputation of Aztechnology, his "employer," to dissuade the runners from making themselves scarce with the down payment. Should the runners do so anyway, the Humanis Policlub is influential and widespread enough to make their lives hell on earth no matter where they go.) If the players want to negotiate with Brackhaven, see the **Negotiation Skill Use Procedure**, page 56, **Shadowrun**.

If the runners request backup, Brackhaven replies that there is no time to arrange it now. The runners should move immediately, and he will arrange for backup to catch up with them en route. In fact, no backup will ever materialize. If questioned about it, Brackhaven will claim that he tried to fix it, but the runners were moving so fast and covertly that his people could not get to them in time.

The dossier on Jesse John contains the following items:
•A photograph of Jesse John. He is a rail-thin man with cold eyes, his sleek black hair pulled back severely into a ponytail. He wears a black leather vest over an open-necked gray shirt. Tight black jeans are tucked into rattlesnake-skin boots. His accessories are all silver: the toecaps on his boots, his belt buckle, a plain band around his right wrist, and a small, finely linked chain that ties back his ponytail. He carries no obvious weapons, but packs

a large assortment of fetishes.

•A document describing Jesse's background. This contains much the same information given in Jesse's character description (in **Plot Synopsis**) except that it fails to mention his connection with the Humanis Policlub. Instead, it describes him as a freelance agent-provocateur.

•A copy of a Salish-Shidhe Council travel pass application bearing the current date under the name of "Ben Johnson." The destination on the application is Las Vegas.

•A fax copy of a Salish-Shidhe Council border-station log. The log shows that "Ben Johnson" crossed the border alone in a Mitsubishi Nightsky several hours ago.

If the runners need transportation, Brackhaven can supply them with a van (Handling 4, Speed 30/100, Body 3, Armor 0, Signature 5, Pilot 1). He can also supply the runners with the necessary visa and travel pass to enter Salish-Shidhe Council lands. (Passport files are the runners' responsibility.) Brackhaven will request 200¥ per person for this service, but a successful Negotiation Skill Test can knock this price down to zero. The visas and passes take one hour to prepare, and the runners must pick them up at a site selected by the gamemaster (a good opportunity to get the runners into some kind of trouble before they even start the mission).

If the team agrees to Brackhaven's offer, get them on the road. Go to **On the Border**, the next section.

Karl Brackhaven

Brackhaven is a handsome, smooth man in his early 40s. He truly believes in the Humanis cause, but he never lets his fanaticism show. Brackhaven has a good education that stressed history and psychology. He knows from historical precedent that the Humanis Policlub must be careful not to go too far. As it stands, many non-members feel some empathy with the club's cause. If the policlub goes over the top and gets involved in a something like war among the NAN nations, and if their involvement becomes known, then they will lose the limited popular support they have managed to build up over the years.

Before making the Central Seattle chapter of the Humanis Policlub his full-time career, Brackhaven was a low-level exec with Aztechnology. This makes it easy for him to convincingly act the role of corporator.

B	Q	S	C	I	W	E	M	R	Armor
4	3	3	5	6	5	2.8	—	4	None

Dice Pools: Defense (Armed) 1, Defense (Unarmed) 1, Dodge 3
Skills: Etiquette (Corporate) 6, Etiquette (Street) 3, Firearms 4, History 5, Negotiation 5, Psychology 7
Cyberware: Datajack, 300 Mp of memory
Gear: Colt America L36 [9 (clip), 3M2], Pocket Secretary, Wrist Phone

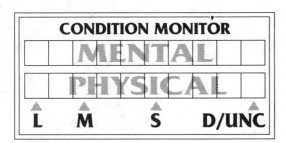

CONDITION MONITOR
MENTAL
PHYSICAL
L   M   S   D/UNC

DEBUGGING

If the team refuses to relinquish their weapons, they can force their way into the lounge, but they will find it empty. (Brackhaven skipped out the back way.) The next day they will receive a repeat invitation explaining that it will be worth their while to shelve their doubts about giving up their weapons. If the characters still refuse to agree to the terms of the meet, pressure can be applied through the runners' contacts: Word on the street says that the team has turned into a knitting circle. Why else would the runners refuse to listen to a simple business proposition?

It is possible that the player characters will turn down Brackhaven's offer. In that case, he will coldly say, "I see I was misled by your street reputation. Well, I'll see to it that nobody else is similarly misled in the future." With that, he will leave by the back door. The Ritz security team is on hand to prevent the runners from following him out of the lounge.

Despite his veiled threat, Brackhaven will not do anything to destroy the runners' rep on the street (but player characters don't need to know that).

Once again, if the team blows off the assignment, they will hear later about another group of runners pulling off a lucrative operation and—supposedly—saving the Native American Nations from war.

ON THE BORDER

TELL IT TO THEM STRAIGHT

Read the following to the player characters when they hit the border.

The border post is just ahead. You've crossed from Seattle, officially UCAS territory, into Salish-Shidhe Council land before, and you're well aware that the Border Patrol personnel in charge of the crossing point don't have much sense of humor. Even though only four lightly armed officers stand outside the blockhouse, you know there are usually at least four of their comrades inside, armed to the teeth and bored enough that they hope you'll start something. (But then again, the paperwork necessary after they'd geeked you would be a real drag.)

You pull up in front of the closed crash-proof gate, and proffer your visas and travel passes. You hope that the paper isn't still warm from the press. The guard examines it, then hands it back. "Everything's in order," he tells you, "but we've got a quarantine in effect. Viral infection in the Seattle area. We're making sure it doesn't get out. I'll have to ask you to park your vehicle over there and step inside the building. Thanks for your cooperation." (The guard's hand resting on the butt of his Ares Predator tells you that he really would appreciate your cooperation.)

If the player characters enter the building, read them the following.

You follow the border guard into the building. With a bare minimum of courtesy, he ushers you into a spartan waiting room, equipped with a chair, a table, and a torn vinyl sofa. There is one door and one window.

"Wait here," he tells you, shutting the door behind him as he leaves. The door closes with a solid, ominous click. Sure enough, when you try the doorknob, it doesn't turn. Locked!

The door may be solid, but it's far from soundproof. You can clearly hear voices from the other side.

"Got' em," says your friendly border officer. "They're not going anywhere."

"Good." You don't know the second speaker, but you do recognize the voice of command. "The UCAS Feds will be here soon, then they won't be our problem any more."

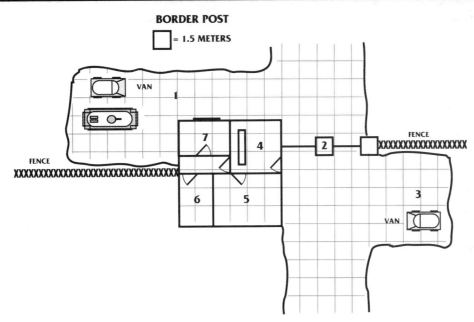

BORDER POST

☐ = 1.5 METERS

BEHIND THE SCENES

The "viral infection" is actually a rather flimsy cover story. The UCAS FBI is at least partially aware of Jesse's plans and his connection with the Humanis Policlub. They believe that the club's leaders support Jesse's aims. The Feds have been following Brackhaven and know the runners are in his employ. The FBI team on the case is small, and they cannot be everywhere at once, so they have called in a couple of markers to get the cooperation of the Salish-Shidhe Council Border Patrol. The Border Patrol has agreed to delay the runners until the FBI operatives can arrive.

The border post is manned by six standard Border Patrol personnel, four outside and two inside, plus a few "surprise guests": a squad of eight Salish-Shidhe Rangers and two Ranger Combat Mages. The Rangers have a Citymaster, which is parked out of sight behind the crossing point.

BORDER STATION MAP KEY

Parking Lot (1)

The parking lot is on the Salish-Shidhe side of the border. Parked in the lot are a van and the Rangers' Citymaster.

Barrier Control Point (2)

One Border Patrol officer is in this booth. The other three outside officers wander around this region, but will converge on any vehicle that approaches the barrier.

Parking Lot (3)

The runners' van is in the parking lot on the Seattle side of the border.

Reception Area (4)

Two Border Patrol officers are behind the reception desk.

Guard Room (5)

The guard room is currently occupied by eight Salish-Shidhe Rangers and two Ranger Combat Mages.

Storage Room (6)

The storage room contains extra copies of customs declaration forms (in quadruplicate), coffee filters, notepads, and other supplies vital to running a customs post.

Waiting Room (7)

See the description of the waiting room under **Inside the Building**.

Border Patrol Officer (Six)

Well-trained and ready for trouble, the average Border Patrol officer will not look for a firefight. His main goal in life is to be able to say that he did his job. In order to successfully defend himself, the officer needs to stay alive.

B	Q	S	C	I	W	E	M	R	Armor
5	4	4	2	3	4	5.5	—	3	5/3

Dice Pools: Defense (Armed) 4, Defense (Unarmed) 4, Dodge 4
Skills: Armed Combat 4, Car 3, Etiquette (Street) 3, Firearms 4, Negotiation 2, Unarmed Combat 4
Cyberware: Smartgun Link
Gear: Ares Predator II [15 (clip), 6M2, with Smartgun Link], Armor Jacket (5/3)

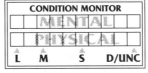

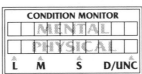

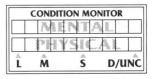

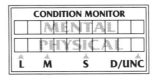

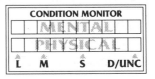

Salish-Shidhe Ranger (Eight)

A Salish-Shidhe Ranger is proud to be a "lean, mean fighting machine." A Ranger will not go out of her way to start trouble, but she sure will not be disappointed if somebody else does. A Ranger always tries to be the one to finish it.

B	Q	S	C	I	W	E	M	R	Armor
5	4	6	3	5	5	4.4	—	4	6/4

Dice Pools: Defense (Armed) 5, Defense (Unarmed) 5, Dodge 4

Skills: Armed Combat 5, Car 4, Demolitions 3, Etiquette (Street) 3, Etiquette (Tribal) 3, Firearms 6, Gunnery 3, Military Theory 2, Stealth 3, Throwing Weapons 2, Unarmed Combat 5

Cyberware: Cybereyes (w/flare compensation), Radio, Retractable Spurs, Smartgun Link

Gear: Beretta Model 70 SMG [35 (clip), 4M3, with Smartgun Link], Heavy Security Armor (6/4, w/o Helmet)

Notes: In addition to the gear listed above, one of the Rangers has a Vehicle Control Rig (for driving the Citymaster) and another carries a Valiant LMG.

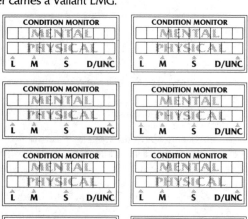

Ranger Combat Mage (Two)

The Ranger mage is a tough hombre with the same kick-butt attitude as his warrior comrades. He is not likely to close with an opponent—but then, he does not have to.

B	Q	S	C	I	W	E	M	R	Armor
4	4	3	3	6	5	6	6	5	6/4

Dice Pools: Astral Defense (as skill)*, Astral Dodge 6*, Defense (Armed) 5, Defense (Unarmed) 5, Dodge 4, Magic 5

Skills: Armed Combat 4, Etiquette (Street) 3, Etiquette (Tribal) 3, Firearms 4, Military Theory 3, Sorcery 5, Stealth 3, Throwing Weapons 2, Unarmed Combat 4

Cyberware: None

Gear: Ares Predator II [15 (clip), 6M2, with Smartgun Link], Heavy Security Armor (6/4, w/o Helmet)

Spells: Detect Enemies 3, Mana Bolt 4, Powerball 5, Power Bolt 3

* See **The Grimoire.**

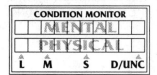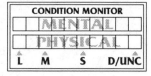

INSIDE THE BUILDING

The door is made of reinforced construction plastic. The Rangers in the other room are alert and ready to take down anything that comes through the door.

The window, on the other hand, is a typical sliding arrangement, and it is unlocked. An alarm is visible on the window, but is clearly broken. The window is in the back of the building. Parked near the window is a nondescript van (Handling 4, Speed 30/100, Body 3, Armor 0, Signature 6, Pilot 1), with the keys in the ignition. (Sure, this isn't a set-up, chummer!)

In fact, the whole situation is a scam within a scam. As the player characters will no doubt conclude, the "viral infection" story is a lie. So is the conversation they overheard about the FBI arriving soon. (The Border Patrol officer and his boss staged that conversation, quite loudly, right outside the door, so the runners could not help but hear it.) If the runners are dumb enough to stay put, the Feds will eventually arrive to interrogate them. But the whole purpose of the exercise is for the runners to escape through the (conveniently unlocked) window and boost the (conveniently unlocked) van, which has (conveniently) been equipped with a powerful location transponder. This device is passive until it receives an interrogation signal from an FBI locator unit, when it responds with a single, high-powered pulse. The van's exact location is read from the device's built-in inertial reckoning system. This device (worth 4,500¥ to the right buyer) is almost impossible to detect because it is passive most of the time. It allows the Feds to locate the runners almost instantly. The Feds plan for the runners to lead them to Jesse. (The Feds are convinced that the runners are actually his back-up muscle.)

DEBUGGING

If the players want to duke it out with the border guards at this point, let them. They will soon learn the error of their ways. The vehicle barriers have a Body Attribute of 6, making them difficult to smash through. All of the Border Patrol officers can engage the player characters the turn after the players start trouble. The Rangers will engage in the following turn. If the runners keep moving through the gate, it will take the Ranger rigger one turn to mount the Citymaster and another turn to get the wheels turning. Then the chase is on. (Remember that the usual Citymaster has a turret-mount coaxial LMG, making it hard, and dangerous, to ignore. The Rangers, not being the types to pussyfoot around, typically load this with explosive rounds.)

If the runners' vehicle is destroyed trying to crash the barrier, which is likely, they will find an unmarked van parked behind the border station.

If the runners are foolish enough to scrap with the border detail and still escape, their lives will be hell during their stay in the Salish-Shidhe Council lands. All-Points Bulletins will be issued, describing the team and their vehicle, and any Council paramilitary officer, Border Patrol, Coast Patrol, or Ranger, will come after them on sight. If any border guards were geeked, standing orders will be "Shoot first and get fingerprints off the corpses."

A smart group of players will bow to the inevitable, park their vehicle, and enter the border post.

GETTING AWAY

Smart players might pass on the "convenient" van. Unfortunately, the only other vehicles available are their own transportation, on the other side of the crash-proof barrier, and—yes, the Citymaster. The Citymaster is secured by a maglock and the ignition is protected by a password system. (A decker might be able to crash into the system through the rigger I/O port, but the system has a Target Number of 8.)

If the runners try to leave by the door, the Rangers will be waiting, locked and loaded and ready to rock 'n' roll. If the players want to do it this way, let them, then let them regret it.

If the runners decide to wait for the Feds, those worthies arrive in 90 minutes. The team comprises Special Agent Clive Drummond, Agent Della Cooper, and six Federal Fast Response Team operatives, packed into an unmarked armored van (Handling 5, Speed 50/150, Body 4, Armor 2, Signature 4, Pilot 2). When they arrive, Drummond immediately interrogates the runners about their involvement with the Humanis Policlub. Even though Cooper disagrees and argues against the possibility, Drummond will quickly conclude that the runners have been set up. The Feds then take the team back to Seattle and keep them on ice until Jesse has been killed or captured. (The runners will have several chances to escape, however, either while on the road or in the slammer.)

At this point, the gamemaster should run **Thunder Road**, the next section, if the runners seem to be taking matters too lightly, or proceed directly to **Wild, Wild West**, p. 22.

Federal FRT Trooper

The Fast Response Team troopers are the elite of the FBI combat arm and they know it. They are fast, mean, chromed, and polished. They always follow orders to the letter, but can act on their own initiative when necessary.

B	Q	S	C	I	W	E	M	R	Armor
5 (7)	4	6	3	4	4	1.1	—	4 (6)	6/4

Dice Pools: Defense (Armed) 5, Defense (Unarmed) 6, Dodge 4
Skills: Armed Combat 5, Car 4, Etiquette (Street) 4, Firearms 5, Stealth 4, Throwing Weapons 3, Unarmed Combat 6
Cyberware: Dermal Plating (2), Radio Receiver, Smartgun Link, Wired Reflexes (2)
Gear: Beretta Model 70 SMG [35 (clip), 4M3, with Smartgun Link], Heavy Security Armor (6/4, w/o Helmet)

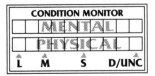

CONDITION MONITOR	CONDITION MONITOR
MENTAL	MENTAL
PHYSICAL	PHYSICAL
L M S D/UNC	L M S D/UNC

CONDITION MONITOR	CONDITION MONITOR
MENTAL	MENTAL
PHYSICAL	PHYSICAL
L M S D/UNC	L M S D/UNC

CONDITION MONITOR	CONDITION MONITOR
MENTAL	MENTAL
PHYSICAL	PHYSICAL
L M S D/UNC	L M S D/UNC

Rick Harris ©91

THUNDER ROAD

TELL IT TO THEM STRAIGHT

You figure that your best bet is a simple speed-run, lead-footing it straight to Vegas. Jesse John, ol' chummer ol' pal, has a good head start and you want to get to the action. So far it seems to be a good decision. The highway's been clear, the run across the Ute a breeze, and you've been able to hammer it all the way down. You're a couple of hours out of Vegas and you haven't hit anything worth worrying about.

But now it looks like you spoke too soon. Several vehicles are heading your way. It looks like a bunch of bikes and maybe a small car or two. They're taking their half of the highway right out of the middle and something tells you this isn't a family outing.

BEHIND THE SCENES

The group approaching is a local go-gang hired and backed up by Humanis Policlub members who support Jesse John. They learned through their contacts at the Seattle Humanis chapter that Brackhaven hired the runners and sent them to Vegas after Jesse. They have decided to head the runners off at the pass.

Eight go-gang members, each riding armed Harley Scorpions, and four Humanis goons in a stolen Westwind 2000 are armed to the teeth and ready to slice and dice.

Go-Gangers (Eight)

These boys and girls are members of the Diamondbacks, a particularly unpleasant gang based in Vegas. They live for the thrill and are willing to die for it as well, as long as they take an "honor guard" with them when they cash in.

B	Q	S	C	I	W	E	M	R	Armor
4 (5)	6	5	4	4	4	5.4	—	5	2/1

Dice Pools: Defense (Armed) 4, Defense (Unarmed) 5, Dodge 6
Skills: Armed Combat 4, Bike 5, Car 4, Demolitions 3, Etiquette (Street) 4, Firearms 4, Stealth 2, Throwing Weapons 2, Unarmed Combat 5
Cyberware: Dermal Plating (1), Hand Razors
Gear: Armor Vest (2/1), TMP SMG [20 (clip), 4M3]

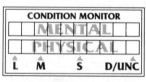
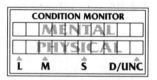
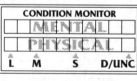
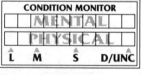

The leader of the Diamondbacks is a nasty character who calls herself "The Edge." In addition to the gear listed above, she packs an Enfield AS7 assault shotgun [10 (clip), 4M3] and two offensive IPE grenades (5S4).

Three of the Diamondbacks (The Edge and her two lieutenants) have Ingram Valiant LMGs mounted to firm points on their bikes.

Humanis Goon (Four)

His greatest joy is chopping up metahumans, Amerindians, mages—basically anyone who does not meet his twisted ideal of "human purity" (in other words, anyone who is not just like him). He will not throw his life away like the go-gangers, but he will give his all in any scrap that he runs even a slim chance of winning.

B	Q	S	C	I	W	E	M	R	Armor
5	4	5	3	3	4	6	—	3	6/4

Dice Pools: Defense (Armed) 5, Defense (Unarmed) 5, Dodge 4
Skills: Armed Combat 5, Car 4, Etiquette (Street) 3, Firearms 5, Gunnery 3, Stealth 3, Unarmed Combat 5
Cyberware: None
Gear: Club (+1 Reach, 6M2 Stun), Remington Roomsweeper [6 (magazine), 3M3]
Notes: In addition to the gear listed above, one of the goons carries an AK-97 Assault Rifle [22 (clip), 5M3].

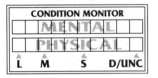

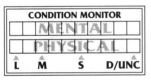

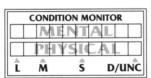

The highway where the runners are is four lanes wide, with no center divider, and should be treated as Open Terrain. The ground on either side of the road is semi-arid scrub and should be considered Normal Terrain. The runners and gang-plus-goons engage head to head. The Edge and her lieutenants will open up with their bike-mounted weapons as soon as the runners' vehicle is in range. The bikers will make a high-speed pass, unloading everything they have into the runners' vehicle, then take up the chase from the rear, trusting to their bikes' high speed to catch up to the runners' vehicle again. The goons in the Westwind will play "chicken" with the runners, opening fire as soon as the runners come into range. They will also take up the chase from the rear.

If the fight turns against them, the goons will cut and run, counting on their firepower and speed to keep the runners off their backs. The go-gangers will fight to the death. If The Edge recognizes that she and her gang will not survive the fight, she will make another head-on pass at the runners, ramming her bike into the front of their vehicle. (Sure she buys it, but she goes down in real style.)

DEBUGGING

This scene is intended to give the runners a taste of the kind of combat glorified in old (pre-simsense) movies like *Mad Max*. It is not intended to geek them all. The gamemaster should try to maintain a careful balance. If it looks like the runners are in trouble, give them a few lucky breaks: a stray shot blows a bike's tire and it crashes into two of its fellows, an overanxious goon takes out a biker, and so on. An experienced group of runners should not need this help, however.

Odds are that the runners' vehicle will be in less than top-notch shape after this encounter. The runners might be able to "requisition" bikes from Diamondbacks who no longer need them or acquire the goons' Westwind. They can also thumb a ride into Vegas. That is, if they can find a driver crazy enough to pick up a bunch of bloody, chromed, street monsters who smell of cordite.

If the goons cut and run, they head back to Vegas and inform the other Humanis members that the runners are on their way. Jesse's supporters arrange a welcoming committee for the runners in **Wild, Wild West**, the next section.

If the runners capture a Diamondback or goon alive, they discover that the Diamondbacks know nothing about Jesse and his plans. They were just hired for a bit of fun. The goons only know that Jesse is in Vegas and that he plans to disrupt the Pueblo Council government. They also know he is looking for a hot decker.

Make the runners realize that they are at a serious disadvantage in upcoming encounters if they fail to obtain intelligence on Jesse's movements. It is time to start working the streets for information. If none of the goons make it back to Vegas alive, go directly to **The Stranger**, p. 24.

WILD, WILD WEST

TELL IT TO THEM STRAIGHT

Vegas, what a place! You thought Seattle was a wide-open town, right, chummer? Well, think again. Compared to Vegas, Seattle is as quiet and conservative as a church picnic. There's something in the air, a vibrancy you've never felt before. The place feels alive with excitement and danger. You pulled into town less than an hour ago and you've already been eyed by more security forces than you thought you'd see in the rest of your misbegotten lives.

They call themselves security forces, anyway. They look more like army: armor, heavy weapons, tactical support, APCs cruising the street, and the occasional rotorcraft gunship cruising overhead. And the "honest citizens" walking the street—they're packing more hardware than you are. But they're not using their weaponry. They don't even seem to notice that they're wearing it, any more than you notice your clothes. This is one wiz town!

BEHIND THE SCENES

This scene takes place only if at least one of the Humanis goons from **Thunder Road** made his escape.

Jesse's Humanis supporters are watching for the runners. They spot the team immediately when they enter Vegas. Humanis has set up a neat, friendly ambush. Five Humanis goons are on the rooftops overlooking the road and one hired razorguy is hunkered down in a doorway, waiting for the runners to roll by. As soon as the runners' vehicle(s) enter the killing zone, the Humanis goons open fire.

For the Humanis goons, use the statistics from **Thunder Road**, p. 21. Instead of Remington Roomsweepers, they pack AK-97s. The rooftops give them Hard Cover against gunfire from the street below.

For the razorguy, use the **Street Samurai** archetype, p. 46, **SR**. When he initially opens up, he has Hard Cover, but he will come out into the open to mop up and run down anyone trying to escape the kill zone.

The Humanis goons have a simple plan: fill the runners and their vehicle(s) so full of lead that they would sink in the Great Salt Lake. If the runners survive the initial onslaught and drive through, or split up and go hunting for the snipers, the goons run. The razorguy is simply hired muscle and will not stick around if the gig goes bad. If he is unable to get away, he will surrender to the runners and hope that the Mercenary's Code, "Don't kill a potential employee," will keep him breathing.

Have each of the team members make a Perception/Intelligence (6) Test before the fun commences.

Successes	Result
1 or less	The street seems quiet until the first high-velocity rounds slam into your vehicle. Frag! You don't even know where the fire is coming from. (Characters with 1 success or less are surprised.)
2–3	Out of the corner of your eye, you see muzzle flashes from the rooftops on both sides of the street just as the first rounds split the air around you. (Characters with 2–3 successes are still surprised, but at least they know where the trouble is coming from.)
4+	Movement on the rooftops! Someone is up there, and the odds are they're not friendly. Light glints off metal and you know you're in trouble. (Characters with 4+ successes are not surprised and enter the Combat Turn through normal initiative.)

Understandably, the Las Vegas security forces resent their streets being turned into a shooting gallery. Twenty Combat Turns after hostilities commence, a squad of eight Vegas Metro heavies arrives. Their main goal is to keep the peace, which in this case means taking down anyone firing off weapons. They would prefer to capture the perpetrators, but they will not waste tears over anyone they are "forced" to geek.

As soon as the Metro boys arrive on the scene, any surviving Humanis goons take off, as does the razorguy.

Vegas Metro Police (Eight)

Well-trained and highly motivated, the Metropol knows his stuff. He is quick to recognize that he and his comrades are outnumbered and cannot handle a protracted fight. Hit them hard and fast is the rule—make the troublemakers incapable of making any more trouble. He is willing to use non-lethal force at first, but if that fails, out comes the heavy stuff.

B	Q	S	C	I	W	E	M	R	Armor
4	4	5	2	3	4	3	—	4	5/3

Dice Pools: Defense (Armed) 4, Defense (Unarmed) 4, Dodge 4
Skills: Armed Combat 4, Car 4, Demolitions 3, Etiquette (Street) 3, Firearms 4, Police Procedure 3, Unarmed Combat 4
Cyberware: None
Gear: Armor Jacket 5/3, Ares Predator [10 (clip), 4M2], Earplug Radio, Helmet (1/1), Low-Light Goggles, Scorpion Machine Pistol [25 (clip), 3M2]
Notes: In addition to the gear listed above, two of the cops carry Net-Guns.

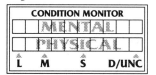 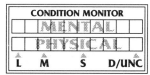 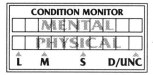 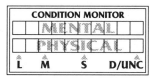 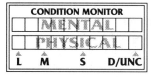 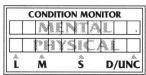 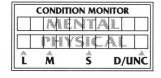

DEBUGGING

The runners should realize that their best bet is to blast through the killing zone at top speed, not sticking around to scrap it out. If they stick around, they have to meet the Metro squad.

If the runners prefer a stand-up fight, odds are that they will have to contend with the Metro squad before they are ready. The squad will capture as many offenders as possible and cart them off for imprisonment and eventual trial. (The Vegas force is professional, and will not engage in any casual sadism against their captives.) The gamemaster should give the runners at least one obvious chance to escape on the way to jail. If the characters miss it, they end up in real hot water. (Refer to **Laws** in the Ute Council source material.)

Enterprising runners may be able to capture one of their ambushers. The razorguy "don't know nothin'"; he is just hired muscle. The Humanis goons know that Jesse is holed up in an apartment hotel called The Kokomo.

THE STRANGER

TELL IT TO THEM STRAIGHT

Okay, you're in Vegas. Jesse's in Vegas. But it's a big city and you need something a little more precise if you're going to track down your target. It's time to start working the streets. If this were Seattle, you'd just talk to your regular contacts. Here, you're a stranger.

Luckily, the streets are pretty much the same in any burg. And the streets are your home. Talk to enough people in the right way, like with a blunt implement or a credstick, and they'll tell you what you want to know.

BEHIND THE SCENES

This scene need only be used if the runners have not found out from other sources that Jesse is holed up at the Kokomo apartment hotel.

This scene gives the players good exercise in using contacts. From a roleplaying perspective, remember that the runners are not on their home turf and will have to work a little bit harder to find out what they need to know. See **Legwork** for how to run the following tables. Three separate tables are available, depending on what information the runners already have. (This will slant their investigation and, presumably, the questions they ask.)

"Work for a Decker" and "The Kokomo" can be used in conjunction if the runners have picked up both relevant pieces of information. If using both tables, determine the number of successes and then reveal the information *from both tables* corresponding to that level of success.

The gamemaster is encouraged to heavily roleplay these scenes.

JESSE JOHN

The runners have not interrogated anybody, and know only that Jesse is somewhere in Vegas.

Appropriate Contacts (Target Number 7)
Any Street Contact

Successes	Result
0	"Who? Jesse what? Look, chummer, Vegas's different, but it's still in tribal lands, got it? Who notices one Amerind more or less—even if he is a slick-looking puppy like you say this one is?"
1	"Gimme that picture again. Yeah, I saw him, jandering down the Strip. Some squatter-type asks him for some ready for a cup of soykaf, and your pal here looks daggers at him. Squatter kinda squeals, then turns and runs like a juggernaut's on his heels. Not a nice boy, your friend."
2–3	"Jesse John, you say his name is? Heard that name on the street. He's hiring, looking for a drek-hot decker. Is that it, you looking for a job? He's interviewing somewhere down on Ghost Wheel Street. Some hotel."
4	"Old associate of mine went looking for a job from this guy. Met him at…the Kokomo, I think that's what he said."
5+	"Drek! That Jesse guy's got some heavy friends hanging around with him."

WORK FOR A DECKER

The runners have learned that Jesse is trying to hire a decker.

Appropriate Contacts (Target Number 6)

Any Decker or Street Contact

Successes	Result
0	"Some guy hiring a decker? Look, babe, everyone around here wants to hire a decker. You got any idea the kind of paydata that's in the Cheyenne system? What about me? You think I look stupid? I want to die in bed with somebody's teenage daughter when I'm a hundred years old."
1–2	"Yeah, he's hiring, and he's not sparing the nuyen on advertising. Some kinda slot-and-run datasteal, I figure. Where? You want to meet with him, you go down to Ghost Wheel Street. Some hotel."
3	"Interviews are going down at the Kokomo. You want the job, you're welcome to it. Hear he geeked one applicant for asking too many questions."
4	"Too late, chummer, he's already got his boy. Calls himself Ram, and he's good."
5	"…and sure as drek he's a certified psycho."
6+	"Heard Ram babbling about going for a major datasteal in the Council financial database."

THE KOKOMO

The runners have learned that Jesse is hanging out at the Kokomo.

Appropriate Contacts (Target Number 6)

Any Street Contact

Successes	Result
0	"The Kokomo? Ghost Wheel Street, I think."
1	"Nice place. Michelin Guide gives it one star…which means you probably won't get geeked in the foyer."
2	"Apartment hotel, goes for longer-term tenants, not by the hour, if you get my drift. Hey, hold the phone. Somebody else asked me about that place earlier today."
3–5	"Oh, yeah, you applying for that decker job? You don't look the type, but hey…Word to the wise, chummer—the guy who's interviewing, he's a real hardcase, and his friends are worse."
6+	"Think you're out of luck, chummer. I heard that the interview's over, job's filled, employer's moved on."

DEBUGGING

The only problem that can arise here is that the runners do not check any contacts at all. Without at least some of the information in this section, progress is going to be difficult.

Remember that the runners are strangers in town. The locals are going to notice it. If the poor bleeders are at sea and need help, one of the local runners could take pity on them and pass them some info that will make their life easier…and probably longer.

The action can move to **The Chase**, p. 26, if the runners are having an easy time of it, or to **Kokomo**, p. 28, if the gamemaster feels the runners have already paid their dues.

THE CHASE

TELL IT TO THEM STRAIGHT

Ghost Wheel Street seems to be the main drag in this part of town. It's wide and well-maintained, lined with expensive shops, fine restaurants, and top-drawer hotels catering to the wealthy business traveler. (Of course, in Vegas, the "wealthy business traveler" probably drives a panzer, not a Nightsky, and deals in mil-spec weaponry, not stock options.) The air is crisp and clean and the chill breeze is refreshing.

As you approach the south end of Ghost Wheel, on the north end of Vegas, the neighborhood changes slightly. The stores are a little less exclusive, the restaurants are now coffee shops, and the hostelries seem to have slipped a star or two. Apartment hotel signs advertise rates by the day, week, or month. This is where you'd expect to find the Kokomo.

"Psst. Hey, chummer." The voice comes from an alley on your right. A squatter-type beckons to you. "You're friends of Jesse, right?" he croaks. "He's moved on. Told me to pass on a message to his friends." He hops from foot to foot impatiently, reminding you of a tattered crow. "Well, get over here. You don't expect me to yell it out loud, do you?"

If one of the team members assenses the area, read the following.

Your perception drifts over toward the squatter...and you damn near run into another astral presence. This one's lean and mean (like you) and ready for action. It's a setup!

BEHIND THE SCENES

The "squatter" is actually a Renraku Field Operative using a mask spell. A Renraku Field Op squad has been following Jesse and his colleagues since Jesse "acquired" certain items from a Renraku Seattle lab (the two prototype tonal generators mentioned in **Plot Synopsis**). The Renraku soldiers have been doing their research and have found out about the runners' contract with Brackhaven and the Humanis Policlub. They jumped to the same conclusion as did the FBI: the runners are helping Jesse in his nefarious plans. There is no direct evidence, but Renraku management has concluded that the runners probably did the snatch-and-grab against their research lab. If so, the runners should still have the tonal generators. Capturing or killing the runners is the fastest way to get their toys back.

A seven-member Renraku squad is hiding in the alley, waiting for the runners to come closer (this number includes the "squatter"). The squad is made up of six Renraku Troopers and one Combat Mage. The mage is currently Astral. Any player character trying to assense the alley will run into her, starting the party. As soon as things get nasty, the mage drops the mask spell.

The Renraku team was about to move in on Jesse when the runners showed, and so they decided to take the runners out first. Simple logic. Wrong, but simple.

The Renraku Field Ops hope that the squatter illusion will sucker the runners into position for a quick ambush. If things get nasty, the squad will disengage and escape to return with more man- and firepower.

From here the team can move on to **Kokomo**, the next section.

Field Operative (Six)

Renraku has trained and equipped him with the best and he is determined that the corporation will never doubt the wisdom of its investment. Though he may not agree with everything the corp does, and may not necessarily be loyal to his senior management, he is exceedingly loyal to his fat paycheck, his medical/dental benefits, and his family's subsidized corporate housing. He will not put his life on the line if he does not have to, but he will not give his squad leader reason to think he was shirking his duty. His orders are to bring the runners in alive if possible, but he and his buddies are not sweating it. If things go bad, they will cut the runners down.

B	Q	S	C	I	W	E	M	R	Armor
4	5	5	3	4	4	1.75	—	4 (6)	6/4

Dice Pools: Defense (Armed) 5, Defense (Unarmed) 3, Dodge 5
Skills: Armed Combat 5, Etiquette (Street) 3, Etiquette (Corporate) 2, Firearms 5, Unarmed Combat 3
Cyberware: Radio, Smartgun Link, Wired Reflexes (2)
Gear: Partial Heavy Armor (6/4), HK227 SMG [20 (clip), 5M3], Low-Light Goggles

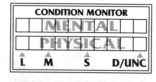

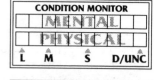

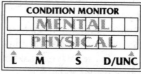

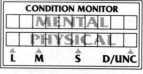

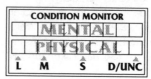

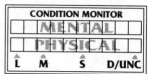

Field Op Combat Mage (One)

She is less gung-ho than her compadres, but dangerous nonetheless. Corporate affiliation means access to grimoires and reference books that she would live an entire life on the street without even being able to glimpse, and she is determined not to blow that advantage without a damn good reason. (Of course, the best hermetic library in the world is no good to someone dead, so this is a condition she will avoid at virtually any cost.)

B	Q	S	C	I	W	E	M	R	Armor
2	3	1	3	5	4	6	6	4	6/4

Dice Pools: Astral Defense (as skill)*, Astral Dodge 5*, Defense (Armed) 3, Defense (Unarmed) 2, Dodge 3, Magic 6

Skills: Armed Combat 3, Conjuring 5, Etiquette (Street) 3, Etiquette (Corporate) 3, Firearms 3, Magical Theory 6, Sorcery 5, Unarmed Combat 2

Cyberware: None

Gear: Heavy Security Armor (6/4, w/o Helmet), HK227 SMG [20 clip], 5M3], Low-Light Goggles, Radio

Spells: Heal Severe Wounds 3, Hellblast 5, Mana Bolt 5, Mask 3, Powerball 5, Sleep 4, Invisibility 3

CONDITION MONITOR			
MENTAL			
PHYSICAL			
L	M	S	D/UNC

DEBUGGING

If the runners are not tough enough to defeat and drive away the Field Op squad, beat them up, work them over, capture them…but keep them alive. The Field Ops realize that the runners are probably not carrying the tonal generators around with them, and so will keep them alive for interrogation.

The Field Op squad has a problem, however. They are in the middle of a strange city with no support, and they need to take a group of dangerous runners to a quiet place and grill them. No matter how cautious the troopers are, the runners should have several chances to escape. The gamemaster should encourage them to take one of those chances.

Of course, it might be the other way around. The runners might end up grilling one or more Field Op troopers. The troopers are front-line grunts, very good at what they do, but not plugged into what their officers are thinking. The troopers know they are after the team to retrieve some high-tech toys the runners stole for Jesse, but they do not know much else. Of course, the troopers refuse to believe the runners' claim that they are not allied with Jesse. ("Sure, chummer, sure I believe you. Of course you're not linked up with that Indian. And please take that pistol out of my ear.")

KOKOMO

TELL IT TO THEM STRAIGHT

The Kokomo is a five-story building with an eye-pleasing Mediterranean design. The front door is flanked by two pygmy palm trees and the steps leading up to the foyer are red tile. As far as you can tell from the street, the lobby is empty.

If a teammember assenses the lobby, read the following.

The lobby is not empty, but the only occupant is a bored-looking desk clerk cleaning his fingernails with a staple-remover. You can tell instantly that the clerk is completely mundane.

But there's something here that isn't mundane, something you haven't experienced before. An astral trail runs across the lobby. You assense it as a gray, cold stain on the floor, leading from the front door to the staircase. The trail assenses of perversion, something powerful twisted out of true. Something magically powerful, and definitely out of the ordinary, has passed this way recently.

If the team enters the lobby, read the following.

As you step inside the lobby, a bored desk clerk puts down the staple-remover he was using as a manicure tool and fixes you with a disinterested stare. "If you're after the job, you're too late," he says flatly. "The man left." He picks up the staple-remover again, then his room-temperature IQ kicks in. "Or did you want a room?"

If the team approaches the room via the stairs, read the following.

Eric the desk clerk watches disinterestedly as you creep up the stairs. (Must be normal behavior at the good old Kokomo.) Soft carpeting silences your tread as you reach the second floor and turn left toward the rear of the building. The hallway is empty and quiet as a grave.

Not quite that quiet. As you approach the door of 2R, you hear voices from inside the room.

"He's getting flaky," the first voice says in an aggrieved tone. "You've seen him, Bob. He keeps changing his mind for no reason."

A second voice, presumably Bob's, growls, "All tribal spellworms are fraggin' flaky." The voice continues more quietly, "Yeah, I hear what you're sayin', Sammy. An' it's worse than you think. I got guard duty outside his room coupla nights back, an' I hear him get into a real drek-kicking argument. I throw open the door, thinkin' he might need some muscle...and he's the only one in the fraggin' room. Almost fried my butt before I could get outta there. He's losin' it. And that Aurora..."

A third voice—female and sharp as a whip—cuts Bob off. "Can it! Aurora's righteous and I don't wanna hear either of you drekheads saying otherwise. Now do the fragging job and let's get out of here."

"Hey, ease off, Liz," Bob whines. "We didn't mean nothin' by it."

If a teammember assenses the building, read the following.

You concentrate on your heartbeat until it becomes a metronome marking the time of your existence. Your body falls away and your unfettered consciousness drifts through the building until you're inside room 2R.

Three figures are in the room, two men and one woman, all big, mean, and loaded for bear. The two men are tidying up and look like gorillas trying to be maids. The woman, a backpack over one shoulder, is closing the drawer of the room's small desk.

"He's getting flaky," one of the men says to the other, the tone of his voice aggrieved. "You've seen him, Bob. He keeps changing his mind for no reason."

The other man, presumably Bob, growls, "All tribal spellworms are fraggin' flaky." He continues more quietly, "Yeah, I hear what you're sayin', Sammy. An' it's worse than you think. I got guard duty outside his room a couple nights back, an' I hear him get into a real drek-kicking argument. I throw open the door, thinkin' he might need some muscle...and he's the only one in the fraggin' room. Almost fried my butt before I could get outta there. He's losin' it. And that Aurora..."

The woman turns on the men. "Can it! Aurora's righteous and I don't wanna hear either of you drekheads saying otherwise. Now do the fragging job and let's get out of here."

"Hey, ease off, Liz," Bob whines. "We didn't mean nothin' by it." The three head for the door, Liz in the lead.

You notice a dark psychic aura to the room. Nothing active, nothing dangerous…more like the psychic equivalent of a lingering odor of decay after something unpleasant has been taken away. It's the same kind of thing you assensed in the lobby. It occurs to you that this might be Jesse's psychic spoor.

BEHIND THE SCENES

KOKOMO ROOM 2R

☐ = .75 METERS

Eric, the desk clerk, is far from a paragon of efficiency, but he does take some parts of his job seriously. For instance, now that the official interviews are over, he is not allowed to tell casual visitors the room in which a guest is staying. If the runners want to learn Jesse's room number, they will have to intimidate or trick Eric, both easy tasks, or look at the register, which Eric keeps behind the desk. Jesse's room is 2R, second floor at the rear.

Eric is probably a career desk-clerk, simply because he is unable to handle anything more challenging. He keeps a holdout pistol under his desk for dealing with trouble, but he will use it only if the danger is so obvious that even he can recognize it. If needed, use the **Pedestrian**, p. 116, **Sprawl Sites.**

The dark psychic trail in the lobby was left by Jesse John and is the first indication the runners have that they are dealing with a Toxic shaman.

The team may decide to approach the room from outside the building. A rickety metal fire escape leads from the ground directly to the window of 2R. (The fire escape looks as though it will creak as soon as someone puts his weight on it. In fact, appearances are deceiving because the structure is solid and silent.) Runners who do not trust the fire escape may try to climb the wall or Levitate up to the window. Let them. When they reach the window, they have a chance to see and overhear the scene described when the runners assense the building. (They will not know about the backpack, drawer, or the "psychic spoor," of course.) Bob, Sammy, and Liz also have a chance to notice the runner(s) at the window. The three Humanis goons get Perception/Intelligence (6) Tests to notice something amiss. The gamemaster should modify this test to account for any precautions the runners take to prevent detection.

If the three Humanis members fail to notice anything, they leave the room by the front door. They are not expecting trouble, at least not yet, so they will be surprised by any runners in the hallway. They will immediately pull their hardware and cut loose. If they spot anyone at the window, they will open up with everything they have. Once hostilities have begun, they will fight to the death.

Bob

Though he is a non-Awakened human—and fragging proud of it—Bob is big and ugly enough to be mistaken for a troll in dim light. (The best way to get on his bad side is to mention this.) He is a dedicated Humanis Policlub member and has sworn to back Jesse with his life if need be.

B	Q	S	C	I	W	E	M	R	Armor
6	3 (7)	6 (10)	2	3	3	1.5	—	3 (5)	2/1

Dice Pools: Defense (Armed) 4, Defense (Unarmed) 5, Dodge 3 (7)
Skills: Armed Combat 4, Etiquette (Street) 2, Firearms 4, Stealth 3, Unarmed Combat 5
Cyberware: Muscle Replacement (4), Smartgun Link
Gear: Armored Vest (2/1), Uzi III SMG [16 (clip), 4M3, with Smartgun Link]

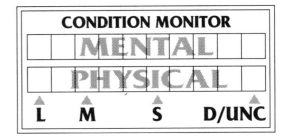

Sammy

Sammy is like Bob but even more so. His muscle bulges have bulges. A long-time steroid abuser, Sammy has somewhat limited mental faculties. Though he has an instinctive skill for violence, when it comes to anything else, he is slightly less intelligent than your average vending machine.

B	Q	S	C	I	W	E	M	R	Armor
6 (7)	2 (6)	6 (10)	1	1	2	.25	—	1 (3)	2/1

Dice Pools: Defense (Armed) 5, Defense (Unarmed) 6, Dodge 2 (6)
Skills: Armed Combat 5, Etiquette (Street) 1, Firearms 5, Unarmed Combat 6
Cyberware: Cyberarm [Right, w/Smartgun Link and Increased Strength (1)], Dermal Plating (1), Muscle Replacement (4)
Gear: Armored Vest (2/1), Uzi III SMG [16 (clip), 4M3, with Smartgun Link]

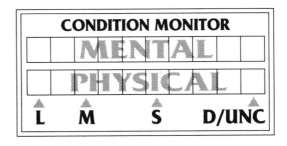

Liz

The intellectual of the group, Liz is a petite blonde with a fine body (all hers). She looks like a cute, harmless airhead as long as she keeps her mouth shut. As soon as she speaks, the snap of command is obvious. Liz's favorite quote is, "Life's a bitch, so I might as well be one." Liz knows the importance of the tonal generator she is carrying and will destroy it before letting it fall into the runners' hands.

B	Q	S	C	I	W	E	M	R	Armor
3	5	3	4	4	3	5.5	—	4	2/1

Dice Pools: Defense (Armed) 4, Defense (Unarmed) 2, Dodge 5
Skills: Armed Combat 4, Etiquette (Street) 4, Firearms 4, Leadership 2, Negotiation 3, Unarmed Combat 2
Cyberware: Smartgun Link
Gear: Armored Vest (2/1), Uzi III SMG [16 (clip), 4M3, with Smartgun Link]

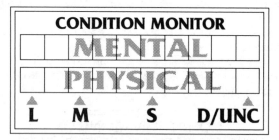

Liz and her buddies are here to plant a little something that will lead the runners into Jesse's trap. This "something" is the microfloppy in the desk drawer. (Liz had just planted it before the runners' surveillance started.) That task completed, they are to take the tonal generator to a meet with Jesse. The runners have arrived a little ahead of schedule and caught the Humanis goons in the act.

THE TONAL GENERATOR

Liz has one of Jesse's two stolen tonal generators in her backpack. This device must be damaged beyond repair in this scene. If bullets fly, all the gamemaster has to do is inform the players that a stray round has struck Liz's backpack. If gunfire does not erupt and the runners try to take the Humanis goons down with magic or trickery, Liz has to resist the magic or see through the scam long enough to draw her gun and put a round into the tonal generator herself. (She knows that her boss' plans will be in serious peril if this device falls into the runners' hands intact.) If neither of these options works out, creative gamemasters should be able to figure out other interesting ways to destroy the tonal generator.

When the team examines what is left of the tonal generator, refer to the information in **Legwork**, p. 62.

THE DATA CHIP

The chip stuck in the back of the desk drawer is a standard optical data-storage device that can be read by any microcomputer or cyberdeck. Reading the chip and understanding its contents are two different things, however. To evaluate the chip contents, a character must have the technical skill related to Computer, or the knowledge skill Computer Theory (or a skill sufficiently close on the Skill Web). The Target Number for evaluating the chip's contents is 3. The amount of information gained depends on the number of successes the character achieves.

Successes	Result
0	Two files are on the chip. One looks like a utility program of some kind, while the other is an encrypted data file. That's all you can figure out.
1	The data file is barely encrypted—nothing more than a cyclical algorithm you could break in your sleep. The file contains a system address, LTG 1303 SAN 0010HF, and a note, "PCC Financial Sub-Net, *Watchdog* monitor alpha." You assume that the system address is where you can break into this "watchdog" monitor…whatever that is.
2	Two versions of the utility program show up. One, the source code, is written in the Q programming language. The other is an executable file, compiled to run on a cyberdeck. The utility is some kind of really elegant, highly specific masking program. The specificity is so great that you're sure this program will work on one and only one SAN in the entire Matrix. Any bets that it's targeted for LTG 1303 SAN 0010AF?
3+	A section of assembly language in the utility source code stumps you for a moment, but you figure out what it is: it writes an identification message into the compiled program. This is not unusual. Lots of programmers do this with copyright notices. But this message is different. It reads, "Wildcat MILCOMP SSF-1284. Military authorized use only."

Players familiar with the Native American Nations will probably guess that this utility is (or is supposed to be) a military-use program developed by the Sioux Special Forces (SSF; the Wildcats) and that MILCOMP is something to do with MILitary COMPuting. If the players do not pick up on this, have each team member make an Intelligence (5) Test to get the idea. Once compiled for use on a specific deck, this utility is 8 Mp.

ADDITIONAL CLUES

A tough team of runners should have no problem taking down Liz and her friends. Either Bob or Sammy—maybe both—will probably get himself geeked. If the runners search the body (bodies), they find a hastily scribbled note that reads:

Jesse—Provo-Under
10127 N. 11th Street
Provo, Ute
[date]

Gamemaster's Note: The date on the note is two days from today. This address becomes relevant in the section **Fascination Street**, p. 40.

Before the team's decker(s) try to penetrate the Pueblo Net, the runners should find a safe physical location where they can hole up. When they are ready to head into the Matrix, go to **Into the Fire**, p. 32.

DEBUGGING

The runners may decide not to investigate Jesse's room. If this happens, Eric suddenly remembers an order Jesse gave him when he checked out. He looks up at the runners again and says, "Wait a minute. You've gotta be the guys Mr. John said would be coming. You want to pick up that stuff he left behind, it's in room 2R. Okay?"

Jesse left this message with the runners in mind. He knows that the team is on his trail and has decided to use them as a tool in his scheme against the Pueblo Corporate Council. The runners have to pick up a certain item that Jesse "accidentally" left behind in his room at the Kokomo in order for this part of his plan to work.

Several other problems can crop up here, mainly if the team simply blows the Humanis goons away and leaves without exploring the room. The team should acquire three things from this scene: a very broken tonal generator, the data chip, and the Provo address. The gamemaster should shamelessly relocate the second two items to ensure that the runners find them. If they search the bodies but not the desk, the chip is in Liz's pocket (she was getting ready to plant it). If they search the room but not the bodies, the Provo address is scribbled on a notepad in the drawer. If they fail to search at all, the chip (in an envelope) is lying on the floor, where it landed after flying out of Liz's hand when she took a high-velocity round. The address is scrawled on the outside of the envelope. (These are just a few possible scenarios.) The runners should be eager to investigate the contents of Liz's backpack, particularly if she fired a round into it herself.

If the team has made some bad tactical decisions and it looks like they are going to get wasted, one or two of the goons can bug out, ostensibly to "warn Jesse what's going down" (not Sammy; he would never think of it). It is not likely, but it is possible that the team could capture and interrogate one or more of the goons. Bob and Sammy have no knowledge about the chip. They were simply sent to cover Liz while she "cleaned up a few things" around the hotel room. They also do not know where Jesse is. When he wants them, he usually gets in touch with them—not vice versa. If questioned, Liz claims that Jesse sent her to make sure nothing important was left behind. She will pretend that the chip was one of the things she was supposed to pick up. She will do everything she can to keep the runners from even considering the possibility that the chip was planted in the room. Liz is not sure that the chip is part of a trap, but she suspects it.

Liz knows nothing about the tonal generator, only that it is very important and that she is supposed to take it to a meet with Jesse later on. (If Liz and friends are "compromised," Jesse will know it and will not show. It is not important if the runners find out where and when the meet was scheduled.) Liz knows that Jesse has hired himself a decker named Ram and that they are making some move against the PCC Financial Database. She has no idea why.

If the runners do not have their own deck or microcomputer, they should run into a dwarf technician who calls himself Thorin (he is an unabashed Tolkien fan) during any legwork they do. He is friendly to anyone who shares his appreciation of well-designed technology, and has a Fuchi Cyber-4 deck, complete with four hitcher jacks, that he is willing to rent to a like-minded friend for only 200 nuyen an hour. (He was repairing the deck, but its owner got herself geeked before she could pick it up.) He has no programs, but he does know some shadow sources if the runners do not have appropriate contacts of their own.

The team will probably want to enter the Matrix, more specifically, Pueblo Corporate Council Net, to try and block Ram. If the runners decide to try tracking Jesse in the real world, rather than in cyberspace, they will be out of luck. No contact can point them in the right direction and no spell can locate the shaman. He seems to have dropped off the face of the earth. In fact, Jesse is drawing on the powers of various toxic spirits to conceal himself. He wants the runners to enter the Matrix, and he is not going to give them any obvious alternatives.

INTO THE FIRE

TELL IT TO THEM STRAIGHT

It's time to try your luck against the Pueblo Net. (Jesse seems to have dropped off the face of the earth, so you've got no other options.) If you can dry-gulch Ram, the psycho decker, in some dark corner of the Matrix, you will put a serious hitch in Jesse John's plans. For Pueblo, at least.

You're lucky that Pueblo is so fully computerized. Virtually every hotel room has an ISDN jack in the wall, allowing you access to the Matrix. (Of course, the hotels are expecting guests to use normal microcomputers that leave identification and billing information every time they access the system. With your highly illegal cyberdeck, you breeze by the billing subroutines as if they didn't exist.)

Now you're into the Matrix, and the virtual horizons of cyberspace expand around you. You can tell right away that you're in an unusual corner of the Matrix. Everything is crisper, more compact. Dataflows are faster and processors are time-slicing at a much higher clock speed. This is the Matrix of your dreams.

At the speed of data, you hurtle down a virtual pipeline to the address on Jesse's chip. Almost instantly, you reach your destination: a fortress with high towers and crenelated battlements. Its black walls hum with power. As you approach the raised drawbridge, a shimmering radiance that looks like heat lightning grows around the fortress. You smell ozone. It doesn't take an analyze spell to tell you that this fortress has really serious security. Now you notice shapes moving on the battlements: huge, hulking silhouettes that remind you of gargoyles. IC, almost surely black. This is not a healthy place to dawdle.

BEHIND THE SCENES

The fortress ahead is SAN 0010AF, the one described on the chip found in Jesse's room. The System Map shows only the smallest section of the Net, the portion dedicated to a simple watchdog subsystem monitoring the operation of a minor accounting sub-module for the Pueblo Parks Board. Various peripheral nodes offer potential access to the rest of the system, but these are of no immediate importance to the decker. (If the decker decides to wander through the rest of the Net, and the gamemaster is willing, further portions of the system can be designed randomly using the method described in **Behind the Scenes**, p. 156, **SR**. As a general rule, the entire Net is Orange or Red Security and rolls for IC are made at +2. If the gamemaster wants to make the rest of the Net off-limits, perhaps for later runs, the system's "adaptive architecture" and serious IC can be used to keep the decker's nose out of things that are none of his business. The Net's adaptive architecture allows anyone with a "key" to change dataline connections. (See **SPU-5**.)

PUEBLO NET SYSTEM KEY

CPU = Central Processing Unit
DS = Datastore
I/OP = Input/Output Port
SM = Slave Module (Slave Node)
SPU = Sub-Processor Unit

SAN-0010AF: Access to the watchdog subsystem from the rest of the Net (the team decker enters the area through here). Red-5, Access 8.
CPU-1: Responsible for the sub-system's watchdog functions. Orange-7, Barrier 7, Killer 5.
SPU-1: File integrity monitor. Orange-5, Barrier 3, Trace and Burn 4.
   DS 1: General ledger account structure. Blue-3.
SPU-2: Numerical co-processor system. Orange-4, Barrier 2, Trace 3.
   DS 3: Real-time performance database. Blue-2.

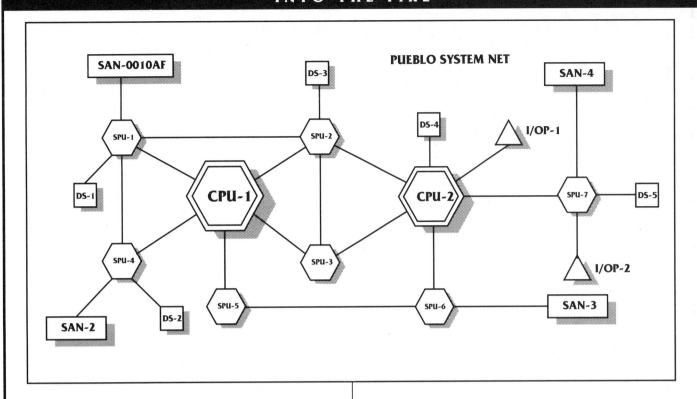

PUEBLO SYSTEM NET

SPU-3: Traffic management co-processor. Orange-6, Barrier 4, Trace and Report 4.

SPU-4: Supervisory coordinator. Orange-5, Barrier 3, Trace and Dump 5.

DS 2: Protocol information for communication between watchdog systems. Orange-1, Scramble 4.

SAN-2: Access to another watchdog subsystem. Red-5, Barrier 5, Blaster 5.

SPU-5: Adaptive co-processor to handle overload conditions on either CPU. Red-6, Barrier 4. The dotted datalines represent an example of the Net's "adaptive architecture." When the team decker enters the system, the dataline connects CPU 1 and SPU 5 and there is no connection between SPU 5 and SPU 6. When Jesse's decker, Ram, triggers his software "key," the architecture changes. Now SPU 5 is connected to SPU 6, not to CPU 1.

SPU-6: Supervisory coordinator. Orange-5, Barrier 4, Trace and Dump 5.

SAN 3: Access to an accounting subsystem. The Pueblo deckers enter the area here. Red-5, Barrier 5.

CPU-2: Responsible for reporting the results of the watchdog functions to the supervisory system and monitoring the performance of CPU 1. Limited Expert System. Orange-7, Barrier 7.

DS 4: Rule base for CPU 2 Expert System. Orange-4, Scramble 5, Tar Pit 5.

I/OP 1: Monitor terminal. Read-only access, designed to give operator a window into the CPU to make sure it is running normally. Rarely used. Blue-2, Access 3.

SPU-7: Traffic management co-processor. Red-5, Barrier 4.

DS 5: Security codes governing access to mid-level supervisory subsystem. Red-4, Scramble 7, Tar Pit 6, Black Ice 3.

I/OP 2: Printer, programmed to print hourly reports on traffic loading to and from SAN 4. Blue-2.

SAN 4: Access to a mid-level supervisory subsystem. Red-5, Barrier 8, Party Ice 3.

ENTERING THE SAN

As described above, SAN 0010AF is Red-5 (in other words, difficult and dangerous to enter). If the decker uses the utility program found on Jesse's chip, however, everything changes. When run, the utility appears as a red and black pennant. As soon as the pennant appears, the glowing, black fortress changes. Its walls become pristine white. Large flags, also red and black, unfurl from the battlements, trumpets sound a fanfare of welcome, and the drawbridge lowers. The decker with the utility and anyone accompanying him is free to enter the SAN. The utility remains active and appears as a pennant hovering above the head of the decker's icon until deactivated by the decker.

DECKER DOGFIGHT

When the team decker enters SAN 0010AF, Ram appears in the SAN at the same time. Ram's icon looks like a huge, black-furred humanoid with glaring red eyes, fangs, and a neon-red "laser" katana. "So you've come to get me, huh?" he snarls. "Then come on. Let's play." Ram triggers a mirrors utility and heads for SPU 5 (via SPU 1 and CPU 1) under cover of the utility. Use the standard pursuit rules, p. 114, **SR**.

When the team decker reaches SPU 5, Ram is standing next to the Matrix construct of the node's barrier IC. As the team decker arrives, Ram gives him a nasty grin and touches the barrier. A siren goes off. (No success test is necessary because Ram *wanted* to sound an alarm. The alarm automatically goes off.)

As soon as he triggers the alarm, Ram attacks the team decker with everything he has for three turns. Then he triggers smoke and mirror utilities and bugs out to CPU 1. As soon as he reaches CPU 1, Ram triggers his "key" program to change the adaptive architecture of the Net. Now, instead of leading to CPU 1, the dataline leads to SPU 6—not a nice place to be at all.

On the fourth turn after the team decker arrives in SPU 5, the turn after Ram bugs out, two PCC deckers enter the system through SAN 3. Their icons look like the "ghosts" from the ever-popular video game Ms. Pac-Man XIX. These guys have all the right passcodes and so can travel freely through the Net. No form of system IC will attack them; however, they cannot control the IC (summon it, direct it, and so on). Their main goal is to dump the intruders as soon as possible and let the system's trace IC give the intruder's physical location to the PCC security forces. This assumes that the intruders are in the Pueblo sector of Vegas. If they are somewhere else, things get problematic.

Both deckers are intimately familiar with the layout of the system. If things get nasty and they have to withdraw, they do so through nodes protected by IC, hoping that the IC will keep their opponents busy long enough for them to make their own escape. If they can, they will also try to herd opponents into heavily protected nodes, hoping that the IC will do their job for them.

PCC Corporate Decker (Two)

The corp decker is young and keen. He decided that service with the PCC Matrix Defense Force was the best way to get his mitts on the cutting-edge hardware and software he dreamed about. He could care less about politics or any of that drek. He follows orders because so far he has been ordered to do things that he would want to do anyway. This assignment is no exception. After all, what could be more of a rush than a good dogfight in a sophisticated system?

B	Q	S	C	I	W	E	M	R	Armor
2	3	1	1	6	3	5.8	—	4	none

Dice Pools: Defense (Armed) 1, Defense (Unarmed) 1, Dodge 2, Hacking 11
Skills: Computer (Decking) 7, Computer Theory 4, Etiquette (Corporate) 2
Cyberware: Datajack
Gear: Fuchi Cyber-5, with Level 1 Response Increase
Programs: Bod 5, Evasion 5, Masking 5, Sensors 5, Attack 6, Shield 2, Mirrors 2.

PUEBLO RESPONSE

Several nodes in the system are equipped with Trace IC. If a Trace succeeds in locating the team's decker, a detachment of Pueblo security soldiers will be dispatched to his physical (real world) location. The detachment will arrive 10 minutes after the Trace is completed and comprises six Pueblo Security Soldiers (use stats from **Wild, Wild West**, p. 23) plus one Company Man (p. 164, **SR**) and a Security Mage (use **Former Wagemage**, Fighter orientation, p. 38, **SR**). Arm them with enough hardware to give the team a good, close fight, but not enough to blow the player characters away. (After all, the Pueblo detachment was expecting a single decker and one or two of his buddies, not a fully armed runner team ready to rock 'n' roll.)

This is how the scene shapes up if the team is operating somewhere in Vegas. If they are not in Vegas, but still within reach of local law enforcement, a Pueblo detachment will arrive in 20 minutes. If they are on somebody else's turf, they will be more likely to break off hostilities when the party gets loud enough to attract attention.

The team should have the address in Provo (if not, see **Debugging**), and will probably be hot to pursue Jesse in that direction. Go to **Rearview Mirror**, the next section.

DEBUGGING

If the team decker gets geeked or dumped, the supposedly Sioux-manufactured utility code will float around in the Net until the Pueblo deckers find it. Without evidence to the contrary, the powers-that-be will consider this proof that the Sioux military is trying to infiltrate their datanets, and that does not sit well with the Pueblo government. (Okay, it was only the Parks Board accounting system, but maybe it was a test run for something more sophisticated.) With this "proof" of interference, the Pueblo Corporate Council will loosen its ties with the NAN Sovereign Tribal Council and move closer to secession, just what Jesse wanted. Because Jesse has achieved one of his major goals, his Threat Rating is increased by +1, making him an even tougher opponent in the final confrontation. (Threat Ratings are discussed in detail in **The Grimoire**.)

Things will look different if Ram is also geeked or dumped. The Pueblo deckers will find his copy of the utility—identical to the code possessed by the "Sioux infiltrator"—except that his is not identified as Sioux military work. No dummies, the Pueblo system managers will put two and two together and realize that somebody is trying to mess with their minds. Though they will be suspicious of Sioux activity for the next couple of months, they will maintain their relationship with the NAN Council and will not make any moves toward secession.

If both Ram and the team decker make it out in one piece, the Pueblo system managers will be completely in the dark about who tried to crash their system and why, unless they manage to trace the team decker and interrogate the runners. Jesse and crew do not want this to happen, so if it looks as if the Pueblo Security Soldiers are going to wipe the floor with the runners, three Humanis goons will enter the fray as equalizers. Use the stats from **Thunder Road**, p. 21, but arm them with Remington 950 hunting rifles. The Humanis goons get off a few pot-shots from hidden positions, dropping enough soldiers to give the runners the edge; then they bug out. (The runners will probably never figure out who was helping them and why. Let them wonder.)

The runners will probably be ready to pick up Jesse's trail again. This time, they have no trouble finding out that he has already hit the road—or, more precisely, the airways—on his way to Provo, Ute. "You mean that crazy shaman? Yeah, some unmarked helijet picked him up downtown, then lit out before the sky marshal could give it a moving violation." If the runners have not discovered the address in Provo, they might learn that information now: "Oh yeah. One of his muscleboys dropped this paper. Some kind of an address, I think." Sharp runners will probably try to track down the owner of the "unmarked helijet," but no information is available.

REARVIEW MIRROR

TELL IT TO THEM STRAIGHT

Things are getting a little hot in the southwest, and you're not talking about the weather. Maybe what you need is a sojourn in a cooler climate. Like Pueblo, for instance?

That requires getting out of Vegas. You're on the street making the arrangements to do just that when all hell breaks loose (again!).

BEHIND THE SCENES

Have each team member make a Perception/Intelligence (7) Test. Anyone who has already met either Special Agent Drummond or Agent Cooper gets a modifier of +1.

Successes	Result
0–1	The first indication you get that anything's wrong is when the doors of a parked car burst open and an amplified voice booms, "Make like ice, boys and girls. *Now.*" (Characters with 0 or 1 success are surprised.)
2–3	You catch movement out of the corner of your eye. Looks like someone's sitting in the parked car you just passed. Suddenly the car doors burst open and an amplified voice booms, "Make like ice, boys and girls…" (Characters with 2–3 successes are not surprised and enter the Combat Turn through normal Initiative.)
4+	Out of the corner of your eye, you see someone move in the parked car you just passed. And—*oh, drek*—you know who it is. (Okay, maybe you don't recognize the face, but you know a high-powered Fed when you see one.) (Characters with 4 or more successes are not surprised and may take one Action before the Feds spring their trap.)

Drummond, Cooper, and one Federal FRT Trooper are packed into a parked Westwind, while six more FRT Troopers are concealed in each of two dilapidated-looking vans (a total of 13 Troopers). These vans are parked 25 meters ahead of and behind the Westwind. Cooper has a miniaturized bullhorn strapped to her throat.

If the team has already persuaded Drummond and the Feds to believe that they are on the side of the angels, their subsequent actions convinced the agent that he made a big mistake. It seems to him that it would be best all around if he were to put the runners away until Jesse has been caught. If the team escaped or avoided the Feds earlier, Drummond is still working under the assumption that the team is acting as Jesse's backup.

As long as Drummond is alive, orders are to capture the runners with minimum damage. Should the team respond to the arrest attempt with lethal force (a likely prospect), the Troopers will get a little more vigorous in their attempts to bring

the runners down, but Drummond will still try to minimize the carnage. If Drummond gets geeked, all bets are off. Under Cooper's direction, the arrest attempt will turn into an execution and the Troopers will do whatever is necessary to take out the runners.

This many Feds armed with this much serious firepower should give the team some very bad moments. Just as things are starting to look grim, another element enters the mix: a group of ten Renraku Troopers (use stats from **The Chase**, p. 26). These guys want the team alive because they still want to sweat the location of the stolen tonal generators out of them. The Renraku Field Ops do not know who the Feds are. They only know what they see, and it looks like they will take the team in, dead or alive. Neither alternative is acceptable to Renraku, so the Field Ops enter the fray to keep their "valuable resources" alive. The Field Ops will try to get the team away from the Feds and capture the runners themselves. The Feds, of course, think that the Field Ops are Humanis colleagues trying to save the runners and so engage them enthusiastically. If the runners are on the ball, they will cut and run while the two other factions work on geeking each other.

TRAVELING TO PUEBLO

Unfortunately for the runners, they do not have access to the convenient transportation services that Jesse seems to enjoy. (One of the disadvantages of not booking ahead…) They have to find their own way to Pueblo. This can be by road or air. Refer to the Pueblo and Ute sections of the sourcebook section for details on transportation and access. Gamemasters can make the journey into a mini-adventure (using the **Highway to Hell** section), or gloss over it by simply telling the players, "You're considerably poorer and sorer as your bus pulls into Provo," and go directly to **Desolation Row**, p. 39.

DEBUGGING

Even though both the Feds and the Renraku troopers could waste the team on their own, they will be too busy wasting each other. The runners should not get geeked unless they try something really dumb. (If they *do* try something really dumb, geek them, and make it good. Stupidity is a capital offense in the **Shadowrun** world.)

If either the Feds or Renraku come out on top, they will try to capture the runners and drag them off for interrogation. The team should have plenty of chances to escape, particularly if survivors from the "defeated" faction are still around to interfere. The Feds will drag the team back to Seattle and lock them up until Jesse has been dealt with. Renraku will take the runners to a deserted warehouse and use various unpleasant methods to try to extract the location of the tonal generators from the team. As soon as they realize that the runners have no clue to the information Renraku wants, they will geek them (so it is important for the team to capitalize on *any* opportunity for escape).

HIGHWAY TO HELL

TELL IT TO THEM STRAIGHT

The Ute-Pueblo border is behind you, and according to your map, it's a straight shot to Pueblo. The highway's in reasonable shape, though the surface is marred here and there by rather puzzling scorch-marks and shallow craters. What's the number of this highway, anyway? Route 666…

BEHIND THE SCENES

This section can be used to liven things up in the unlikely but possible chance that the team has somehow managed to avoid serious combat thus far in the adventure. It is also a good way to bleed off large supplies of ammo, degrade wiz equipment, remind the runners that Vegas and Seattle are not the only dangerous places on the continent, and generally indulge in gratuitous violence.

Have each team member make a Perception/Intelligence (7) Test.

Successes	Result
0–1	Kaboom! With absolutely no warning, *something* detonates impressively in front of your vehicle. Shrapnel rattles off metal, but there's no obvious damage done. (The explosion left a small scorch-mark on the road. Aha.) Now, where the drek did that explosion come from? (Characters with 0 or 1 successes are surprised. Unless they state that they are looking up, they must make another Perception/Intelligence (5) Test next turn or be surprised again.)
2	Your peripheral vision shows you a flicker of movement…*above* you? (Characters with 2 successes are not surprised, and enter the Combat Turn through normal Initiative.)
3	What the frag was that? There's something above you, sandy-brown with a human-sized body and a good five-meter wing span. (Characters with 3 successes are not surprised and may take one Action before the enemy flying above them can act. **Gamemaster's Note:** The characters *are not* immediately aware of the enemy's true nature.)
4+	Your subconscious alarms trigger. Something's watching you. You look left, right, up. There it is, swooping down on your vehicle from overhead. For a split second, you think it's some weird airborne monster, but then your brain makes sense of what you're seeing. It's a guy in a hang-glider or ultralight in a shallow dive directly above you and paralleling your course. And he's got something in his hand. (Characters with 4 or more successes are not surprised and may take one Action before the enemy can act.)

Flying above the runners' vehicle(s) is a go-ganger in a tiny ultralight aircraft (Handling 3, Speed 25/70, Body 1, Armor 0, Signature 1, Pilot 0). The pilot is completely exposed in this vehicle, so shots targeted at him are unaffected by the structure of the ultralight itself. The pilot carries six defensive grenades slung on a bandolier and plans to use all of them against the runners. The pilot is a go-ganger, but he is not an idiot. He knows that in his ultralight he is hung out to dry if his targets return serious fire. As soon as the lead starts flying, he pitches one last grenade then makes himself scarce.

The ultralight pilot is a member of the Beasts, a particularly nasty go-gang that claims this part of Route 666. While the pilot is distracting the runners, the other members of the gang are tearing toward the team's vehicle(s) in a high-speed head-on assault.

Ten Beasts are mounted two-up on five Harley Scorpions. The Beasts riding behind the drivers are "gunners" and are more heavily armed. The bikes have no mounted weapons.

The Beasts will abandon the fight if it turns into a losing battle. They will make their escape heading away from Provo, forcing the runners to backtrack if they want to pursue. Whatever the outcome, go to **Desolation Row**, the next section.

Beast (Ten)

A typical go-ganger, he is out for some fun at the expense of anyone who gets in his way. Because this stretch of Route 666 is his territory, any fun he has is going to be fatal to his playmate.

B	Q	S	C	I	W	E	M	R	Armor
4	5	4	3	3	4	5.7	—	4	—

Dice Pools: Defense (Armed) 4, Defense (Unarmed) 4, Dodge 5
Skills: Armed Combat 4, Bike 4, Etiquette (Street) 4, Firearms 4, Stealth 2, Unarmed Combat 4
Cyberware: Cybereyes (Low-Light), Hand Razor
Gear: Browning Max-Power Heavy Pistol [8 (clip), 4M2], Knife (2L1), Remington Roomsweeper [6 (magazine) 3M3, used by "gunners" only]
Notes: In addition to the gear listed above, one of the bike "gunners" has a monofilament whip (Reach +2, 6S4, Target Number 5) which he will attempt to use against any exposed team member.

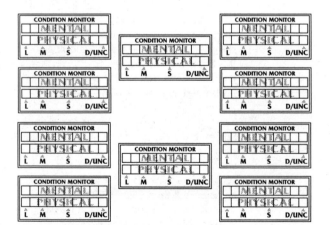

DEBUGGING

As with the earlier *Mad Max* section, the team may be outgunned and could get themselves geeked here. If this is the case, the gamemaster should decrease the number of Beasts, make them lousy shots, or give the team an advantage. (For example, the Beasts' shotguns tear huge hunks of metalwork off the runners' vehicle, but do little or no damage to those inside.) A lucky shot by a runner might detonate a bike's fuel tank, causing a fiery pile-up and wasting several Beasts, with only one round expended. The monowhip also presents a great opportunity for a little mayhem.

DESOLATION ROW

TELL IT TO THEM STRAIGHT

As you roll into Pueblo, you realize immediately how different it is from Vegas. The most noticeable difference is the number of Anglos on the streets—zero. The locals are watching you with the same flat, emotionless gaze that you imagine a rabbit sees in the eyes of the snake. (There's no overt hostility, but you'd sure as drek feel more comfortable if your skin were a different shade and you had a few feathers in your hair.) Sizing you up as possible opponents, the Security Force "cops" you pass give you a similarly calculating stare.

Other differences become obvious. Gone is that edge of hair-trigger danger, that ambience of the wild West that you felt in Vegas. Not to say that Pueblo's a safe haven, of course. Any new city has its dangers, even without Jesse.

And that's the next order of business. Track down the man, stop the man, collect your pay. Then it's back to Seattle and familiar dangers.

BEHIND THE SCENES

The first thing the runners must try to do is investigate the address they acquired in Vegas. Anybody familiar with the city can tell them that the address is in what used to be the light-industrial and warehouse district. Most of the businesses have closed down or moved, and the deserted warehouses and small factories have become a haven for squatters. Nobody the team talks to can explain what is significant about the specific address, however.

The team also needs to find out about "Pueblo-Under." Because Pueblo is a new and unknown city, tracking down appropriate contacts will be another good opportunity to develop roleplaying skills. See **Legwork** for more about Pueblo-Under and the Underground Awakened.

DEBUGGING

The team may be consistently skunked while trying to track down contacts and information. If the players have been roleplaying well but just cannot get a break, consider fudging the dice rolls. If they are not working hard enough—too bad, they will have to go in blind.

When the runners are ready to investigate the address they picked up in Vegas, go to **Fascination Street**, the next section.

FASCINATION STREET

TELL IT TO THEM STRAIGHT

No matter where you go in the world, if you've seen one warehouse district, you've seen 'em all. You might be in Vegas or Seattle instead of Pueblo. Wide, dirty streets, grimy buildings, and a constant, low level of truck traffic 24 hours a day.

Your destination, 10127 North Eleventh Street, looks the same as the other warehouses surrounding you, except that it's a little more dilapidated. A crooked sign identifies it as belonging to Jones Chain and Wire. From the general disrepair of the building, you surmise that Mr. Jones fell on some hard times.

If one of the team members assesses the warehouse, read the following.

As you slip into astral, your perception drifts through the wall of the building. It's empty, you sense that at once: nothing larger than a couple of rats is alive in here. But there's something else—the same "spiritual taint" you assensed in Vegas. It's faint, as though the source hasn't been around for a while, but it's definitely there.

Read the following to the players when they descend underground.

The steep staircase leads down into a dimly lit tunnel uncomfortably reminiscent of a sewer. You hesitate for a moment—which way do you turn?—but then you notice the caress of fresh air on your face from the west. The gentle breeze carries a murmur of voices and a gentle aroma. *Flowers?*

You move cautiously through the tunnel to the west. The undercurrent of voices grows louder; it sounds like a town meeting or some such drek. Almost at the same time you figure this out, you notice the tunnel you are following. The walls and floor are dry and look almost scrubbed. Dim lights are mounted at regular intervals along the ceiling. You realize that the floor is slightly slanted and you are continually moving deeper underground.

The tunnel turns a corner…and you duck back behind cover. Cautiously you peer out.

You're looking into a large room, maybe 25 meters or so square, with a ceiling almost 10 meters high. The room is brightly lit—it seems like sunlight—and it's filled with a riot of color that reminds you of an Impressionist painting of a park. People mill around the room. Welcome to Pueblo-Under.

If one of the team assenses the tunnel area, read the following.

Your astral body drifts silently and invisibly along the tunnel. As you turn a corner, you see a small, amorphous mass that looks like congealed garbage. It takes you a moment to realize that the mass is astral. A city spirit, you guess. The spirit watches you with mismatched eyes that constantly change shape and color. It's not hostile, merely curious.

If Joey is escorting the team, read the following.

Joey runs out from cover, waving his arms and yelling, "Hey, guys, look who I've brought." Dozens of pairs of eyes fix on you.

BEHIND THE SCENES

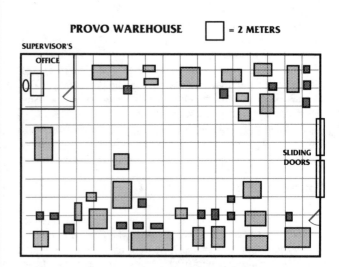

PROVO WAREHOUSE ☐ = 2 METERS

SUPERVISOR'S OFFICE

SLIDING DOORS

Heavy machinery for making chain and extruding wire is still bolted to the cement floor. Spools of wire are stacked everywhere. A patina of rust lies over everything metal and dust covers the floor. The high ceiling is supported by two rows of heavy steel girders.

The building is deserted (but the runners do not know that). No alarms are visible and the doors are all unlocked. This is a great opportunity for the gamemaster to work on the players' fears. A deserted warehouse can be a really spooky place, especially at night, and the danger always exists that someone or something is going to leap out and geek the runners.

While the runners are exploring the warehouse, someone enters the building, but not through any of the usual doors. The runners see movement inside the windowed supervisor's office. They cannot tell exactly what is moving around in there, but it looks human.

The movement the runners saw was an ork named Joey, a member of the Underground Awakened tribe. He was not aware that anybody was in the building, and the encounter will surprise him as much as the runners.

Trigger-happy runners are quite likely to pop off a few rounds at anything that moves, just on principle. As the first shots smash through the glass window of the office, Joey hurls himself behind a heavy metal filing cabinet, screaming, "Hey,

▼ ▼ ▼ ▼ ▼ ▼

don't kill me, don't kill me!" The first volley of firing should not harm the young ork (lucky, lucky). But if the runners want to follow him into the office and finish him off there, let them. Give Joey a chance to whimper and plead for his life, however. (Killing Joey will lose the runners an excellent guide, cost them some Karma, and put them in a bad position when dealing with the other Underground Awakened, but they do not know that. Let them suffer for their itchy trigger fingers.)

Joey—assuming he is still alive—will not volunteer to take the team down into Pueblo-Under, but if they ask, he will agree to be their guide. The entrance to the underground tunnel is beneath the manager's desk, which is bolted to a slightly raised platform. The platform slides smoothly on silent runners to reveal a stairway leading down.

Joey

In his early teens, Joey is the kind of smart-talking, twerpy kid that should be kept away from society until he is 21. He is an ork, however, and orks reach physical, if not emotional, maturity very young. (Imagine your neighbor's snotty kid in an adult body.) Joey is a member of the Underground Awakened and so he can answer any of the team's questions about the tribe (but all of his comments will be filtered through the perception of a 13-year-old).

B	Q	S	C	I	W	E	M	R	Armor
2	5	2	3	3	3	6	—	4	none

Dice Pools: Defense (Armed) 1, Defense (Unarmed) 2, Dodge 5
Skills: Etiquette (Street) 3, Etiquette (Tribal) 4, Unarmed Combat 2
Cyberware: Smartgun Link
Gear: Collection of Urban Brawl trading cards, "Neil the Ork Barbarian" action figure, a well-viewed picture torn from *Playork* magazine.

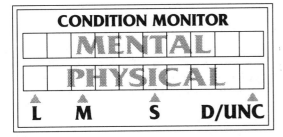

UNDERGROUND

The team has blundered into a council meeting of the Underground Awakened tribe. These meetings are comfortably informal and led by the tribal chief, Mary Hawkmoon. Mary, a troll, loves this room—a hydroponic garden that helps keep the air clean in Pueblo-Under—and holds most council meetings here. The other eight members of the council are present, along with spectators. (Mary believes that tribal business should be open to anyone interested.) All attendees are orks or trolls.

At the entrance to the garden room is a City Spirit with a Force Rating of 6. It is currently astral, making it invisible to anyone not assensing the area. Mary Hawkmoon summoned the spirit and ordered it to act as sentry. It will attack only if someone tries to harm the tribe members within. Unless the runners are hostile, the spirit will simply follow and observe them. (It seems to be somewhat curious.)

The team's reception depends on how they treated Joey in the preceding encounter. If Joey leads them in and introduces them, they are greeted politely. Mary Hawkmoon and the others will answer any questions willingly, as long as those questions are phrased politely. If the team arrives without an escort, the tribe reacts with suspicion and barely concealed hostility. The orks and trolls just want the runners out, and will be unwilling to answer even the least-nosey questions. If the characters want any cooperation at all, they must roleplay the encounter very carefully or get lucky with Interrogation, Negotiation, or Etiquette Tests.

Anyone in the meeting can provide the following information: The Underground Awakened tribe is a generally peaceable group that concentrates on making a life for themselves. Goblinization made it impossible for most of them to stay with their old tribes, so they congregated in a new tribal organization dedicated to reconciling the old ways with their Awakened nature. Neither Mary Hawkmoon nor the other council members know anything about Jesse John or any contact between the shaman and the tribe. If the runners ask about tribal involvement in BTL dealing, Mary reacts strongly. The Underground Awakened live by the rules of their own tribe and of the nation of which they are a part, she declares. She does admit having heard rumors about a small group within the tribe involved in BTL trafficking without the sanction of the council or the rest of the tribe. Mary is not sure of the identity of these people, and certainly will not give names to the runners based on hearsay. If the team asks for help in fighting Jesse, Mary refuses. He is not the tribe's concern and she has no evidence that John has broken any laws, tribal or national. She will, however, volunteer Joey as a guide to lead the runners out of Pueblo-Under. She will strictly forbid them to explore other parts of the underground community, insisting that they leave the way they came. The runners would only get access to other parts of the community under the following circumstances.

When the team starts questioning Mary and the others, have each runner make a Perception/Intelligence (6) Test.

Successes	Result
0	No information. (Don't tell them a thing!)
1	Out of the corner of your eye, you glimpse movement near one of the tunnel entrances. (The character can do nothing this turn, but can react on the next turn.)
2–3	At the back of the crowd, you see a small ork pushing his way toward one of the tunnel entrances. (The character can react this turn following the normal Initiative rules.)
4+	A small ork is pushing his way through the crowd, heading toward one of the tunnel entrances. You didn't think anything about it at the time, but now you recall the same ork had been working his way toward you when you started to question the tribal council. (The character may take one action before the ork is able to leave the room.)

The commotion is caused by a young ork named Zachery, one of the malcontents involved in the BTL trade. He has learned that the runners are asking questions about Jesse, and he figures he had better pass that information on to the other members of his group. Zachery will try to use what little stealth he can muster to make his getaway without being detected. If pursued, however, he will run. Unless the runners catch him, Zachery will reach his compatriots and they will set up an ambush for the team; go to **Crossfire**, p. 43. If the team captures and interrogates Zachery, they can orchestrate a less violent meeting with the malcontents; go to **Smuggler's Blues**, p. 45. If Mary Hawkmoon hears Zachery's confession, she will agree to let the team visit the ork's partners in crime.

If the runners notice Zachery and go after him, he will run. If he is cornered, he will fight until threatened with serious hurt, then he will surrender and beg for his life. Assuming the player characters let him live, he leads the runners to the meeting place of the Barrelhouse Boys, as described in **Smuggler's Blues**. That section also contains the background information the runners can extract from Zachery if they interrogate him. If the team failed to notice Zachery, or did not chase him, go to **Crossfire**, the next section.

Mary Hawkmoon

Mary is the daughter of an influential subchief, but her goblinization made it impossible for her to remain with her tribe. She is big and ugly—a typical troll—but something about her manner is reminiscent of a kindly (but strong-minded) young woman. Mary was chosen as chief of the Underground Awakened because of her ability to orchestrate consensus and compromise between conflicting factions. She has dedicated her life to protecting and strengthening her new tribe and is the implacable enemy of anyone who seeks to do that tribe harm. Mary is a shaman of the Dog totem.

B	Q	S	C	I	W	E	M	R	Armor
8	3	8	3	4	4	6	6	3	none

Dice Pools: Astral Defense (as skill)*, Astral Dodge 4*, Defense (Armed) 1, Defense (Unarmed) 2, Dodge 3, Magic 4
Skills: Armed Combat 2, Conjuring 6, Etiquette (Street) 1, Enchantment 3, Etiquette (Tribal) 6, Firearms 4, Magical Theory 2, Sorcery 4, Stealth 1
Cyberware: None
Gear: Knife (4L2), Medicine Lodge Material, Reusable Detection Fetish
Spells: Detect Enemies 3, Mana Bolt 4, Powerball 5, Power Bolt 3
*Per **The Grimoire**.

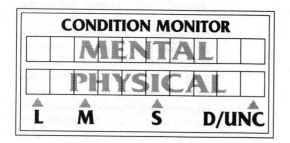

Zachery

An ork, about 25 years old, Zachery is a member of a group that calls itself "The Barrelhouse Boys." (The origin of this name is obscure and nobody outside the group uses it or knows of it.) The Barrelhouse Boys are involved in the lucrative BTL trade between the Sioux nation-underworld and local buyers. (Details of the Boys' activities are given in **Crossfire**.) Physically, Zachery is a small, sneaky, abject coward.

B	Q	S	C	I	W	E	M	R	Armor
2	4	1	1	2	2	6	—	3	2/1

Dice Pools: Defense (Armed) 1, Defense (Unarmed) 4, Dodge 4
Skills: Armed Combat 1, Etiquette (Street) 2, Etiquette (Tribal) 2, Firearms 1, Stealth 2, Unarmed Combat 4
Cyberware: None
Gear: Armor Vest (2/1), Colt America L36 Light Pistol [9 (clip), 3M2], Knife (1L2)

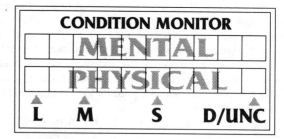

DEBUGGING

Whether the runners shoot or otherwise mistreat Joey will affect the tenor of their next encounter. If the team arrives among the Underground Awakened led by an enthusiastic Joey, their reception will be cordial and generally helpful; if they arrive alone, or with a wounded Joey, the reception will be considerably cooler.

If Joey is killed or otherwise unable to tell the team about the entrance to Pueblo-Under, the team will discover the supervisor's desk partially pushed back, exposing the stairway, when they investigate his office. If, for some reason, the team does not want to investigate the stairway, give them a reason: tantalizing, distant conversation below, or the approach of a regular security patrol above.

The team might try to geek everyone in sight. Not a good idea. There are 24 Underground Awakened in the garden room, in addition to Mary Hawkmoon. Ten of them are trolls (use the **Troll Bouncer**, p. 173, **SR**), eleven are ork tribe members (use the **Ork Mercenary**, but cut back on the hardware, p. 41, **SR**), and three are ork shamans (use the **Street Shaman**, p. 47, **SR**). If they decide that the team has come to destroy their tribe, they will geek first and ask questions later. The city spirit summoned by Mary will attack the runners if they start trouble.

If the team geeks Zachery, the gamemaster has two options. The first is to run the runners through the ambush in **Crossfire**. The second is to find some other way of providing the team with the location of the other Barrelhouse Boys. (Perhaps Zachery was carrying a note, or maybe one of the other tribe members knows where Zachery and his "no-account friends" usually hang out.) Remember that geeking Zachery without reasonable provocation will get the team in dutch with the other members of the Underground Awakened.

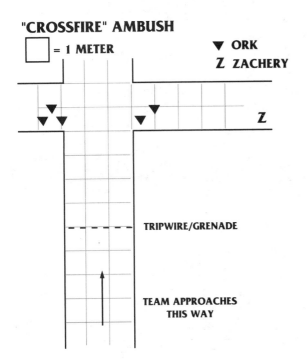

CROSSFIRE

TELL IT TO THEM STRAIGHT

You follow as your guide moves down the tunnel ahead of you. The ork turns to call something back to you and suddenly his body is engulfed in an explosion.

"CROSSFIRE" AMBUSH

☐ = 1 METER

▼ ORK
Z ZACHERY

TRIPWIRE/GRENADE

TEAM APPROACHES
THIS WAY

BEHIND THE SCENES

The guide has tripped a booby trap set by the Barrelhouse Boys. The trap was a simple defensive grenade rigged to a tripwire. The guide was only about one meter away from the grenade when it detonated. The effects suffered by the team depend on how far behind the guide they were.

As soon as the grenade goes off, the Barrelhouse Boys toss two offensive grenades and open fire. The five orks are hiding around the corners of a cross-tunnel (see map) and so have partial cover. Zachery the ork is present, but he will stay clear of the battle and will keep his head safely down.

The Barrelhouse Boys are not used to fighting and are pretty bad at it. (In fact, they are horrified by the effect of their grenades and weapons.) If the fight turns against them, they will run away or surrender.

BARRELHOUSE BOYS

The "Boys" are six orks (including Zachery) and a troll named Crunch who have a lucrative little business going in Pueblo-Under. Through their street contacts, the Boys found out that the Sioux nation underworld was looking for "local representatives" to distribute their illegal BTLs. The Boys accepted this marketing assignment and have been doing fairly well. (Or so they think; in the grand scheme of things, they are actually small fish.) They initially got into the business more for the thrill than anything else. Several months ago, when the Pueblo police started clamping down on the BTL trade, the Boys' Sioux contacts suggested they get some weapons. The six orks began to feel that things were getting a little too heavy at this point, but Crunch, who is as hard as the other Boys like to pretend they are, persuaded (and intimidated) them into sticking it out.

The situation has gotten worse recently. Crunch has been talking crazy, like something twisted his mind. A few days ago, he told the other Boys that a high-ranking military officer from the Sioux Special Forces had contacted him for a special assignment of great importance. He made the other Boys swear a blood oath to do everything in their power to protect their secret operation, and that includes geeking anyone who comes sniffing around. By now, the Boys are quite sure that Crunch has gone mad, but he put enough of a scare into them that they go along with his demands. Now Crunch is off pursuing his "secret mission" and the other Boys are on their own.

If the runners interrogate any of the surviving Barrelhouse Boys, the orks will be only too glad to explain all this and get it off their chests (particularly if one or more of their number has been badly wounded or killed). The Boys know nothing about Jesse John and none of them has met Crunch's "Sioux military officer." From Crunch's description of the officer, however, the Boys admit that he and Jesse might well be the same person. If the runners ask, the Boys will tell them that Crunch rents a room at the Carlisle, an apartment hotel in the low-rent district of Pueblo. The address is Center Street and Fourth West, Room 12.

The team can easily find out that the Carlisle is a cheap apartment hotel and that Center and Fourth West is a nasty corner of town. When the team is ready to investigate The Carlisle, go to **Heartbreak Hotel**, p. 46.

Barrelhouse Boy (Six)

In his early 20s, he is scared stiff at the way his simple distribution deal has spun out of control. Obeying the instructions of the terrifying Crunch, he has reluctantly decided to use force to protect his secret. The death and destruction caused by the simple grenade trap horrifies him, but he feels as if he has committed himself and so opens fire. Fear soon takes over, however, and he is glad to surrender and confess.

B	Q	S	C	I	W	E	M	R	Armor
3	3	2	2	2	6	—	2	3	4/3

Dice Pools: Defense (Armed) 1, Defense (Unarmed) 1, Dodge 3
Skills: Armed Combat 1, Etiquette (Street) 2, Etiquette (Tribal) 2, Firearms 1, Stealth 2
Cyberware: None
Gear: Armor Vest (w/plates), Knife (1L2), Ruger Super Warhawk Heavy Pistol (6 shots, 4M2)

CONDITION MONITOR	CONDITION MONITOR	CONDITION MONITOR
MENTAL	MENTAL	MENTAL
PHYSICAL	PHYSICAL	PHYSICAL
L M S D/UNC	L M S D/UNC	L M S D/UNC

CONDITION MONITOR	CONDITION MONITOR	CONDITION MONITOR
MENTAL	MENTAL	MENTAL
PHYSICAL	PHYSICAL	PHYSICAL
L M S D/UNC	L M S D/UNC	L M S D/UNC

DEBUGGING

Even if the runners kill off the other five Barrelhouse Boys, the cowardly Zachery should manage to keep himself alive long enough for the team to interrogate him. Zachery can be an amusing way for the gamemaster to give the team vital information (for example, if the players fail to ask about Crunch's whereabouts, Zachery can blurt out the facts…and receive fierce looks from his compatriots for volunteering information). If a particularly enthusiastic team manages to geek everybody, they can still learn the location of Crunch. One of the Boys has a note in his pocket:

> The Man's got some big plan for me, something about his secret assignment. You guys better cover your sorry butts while I'm gone. If you gotta contact me, I'm at the Carlisle, Center St. and 4th West, #12. And it had better be fragging important.
> —Crunch

SMUGGLER'S BLUES

TELL IT TO THEM STRAIGHT

According to your information, the Barrelhouse Boys' hideout is just around the next corner. As you move slowly forward, you hear voices.

If the team reconnoiters physically, read the following.

You move forward until the voices become clearer.

"I don't like it," a young male voice snarls. "That Crunch, he's crazy, chummer. Real fragged in the head."

"Rick's right," a quieter voice echoes. "This is too heavy. I want out."

"Yeah. Yeah, right." The third voice drips with sarcasm. "You want out. Frag, I want out. But I'm not drek-headed enough to tell that to Crunch. You want to tell him?"

Silence.

If a teammember assenses the area, read the following.

Your astral self floats out of your body and drifts forward. Just around the corner is a small room. Five young male orks are present, obviously engaged in an important discussion.

"I don't like it," one of the orks snarls as he paces nervously. "That Crunch, he's crazy, chummer. Real fragged in the head."

"Rick's right," another echoes quietly. He's leaning against a wall, shoulders hunched as though he'd like to curl up and hide. "This is too heavy. I want out."

"Yeah. Yeah, right." The largest of the five orks is sprawled in a chair. His posture is casual, and the other orks probably believe the facade, but you can tell he's almost vibrating with tension. His voice drips with sarcasm. "You want out. Frag, I want out. But I'm not drek-headed enough to tell that to Crunch. You want to tell him?"

Silence.

BARRELHOUSE BOYS HIDEOUT

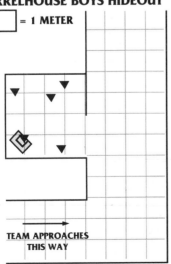

☐ = 1 METER

**TEAM APPROACHES
THIS WAY**

BEHIND THE SCENES

The five orks are the other members of the Barrelhouse Boys. In their home base they do not expect trouble and so only one—the largest ork, sprawled in a chair—is armed with a Ruger Super Warhawk Heavy Pistol. When the runners make their move, this ork will fire off two shots, then throw his gun down and surrender. The other four orks will surrender immediately. The statistics for the Barrelhouse Boys can be found in **Crossfire**, p. 44.

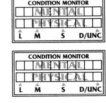

Hidden around the room are the Boys' other weapons: four Ruger Super Warhawks, one defensive grenade, and two offensive grenades. The runners can also find a stash of BTLs. (This stash is small and contains only light entertainment. This should reemphasize just how small-time the Boys really are.)

Assuming the team has allowed at least some of the Boys to live, they may interrogate them. The information available is detailed in **Crossfire**.

The team can easily find out that the Carlisle is a cheap apartment hotel, and that Center and Fourth West is a nasty corner of town. When the team is ready to investigate the Carlisle, go to **Heartbreak Hotel**, the next section.

DEBUGGING

As in **Crossfire**, if a particularly enthusiastic runners' team manages to geek everybody, they can still learn the location of Crunch. One of the Boys has a note on his body:

The Man's got some big plan for me, something
about his secret assignment. You guys better
cover your sorry butts while I'm gone. If you
gotta contact me, I'm at the Carlisle, Center St.
and 4th West, #12. And it had better be fragging
important.
—Crunch

HEARTBREAK HOTEL

TELL IT TO THEM STRAIGHT

The Carlisle is a few notches below the Kokomo in Vegas for quality, maybe half a step up from "flophouse." (Here, the rats and cockroaches only make their appearance after dark.) There's no sign of life in the lobby and nobody behind the reception desk. (A sign reads "Ring bell for service," but someone has thoughtfully stolen the bell.) A small map showing the building layout—presumably for the edification of firefighters, paramedics, and hit men—shows that room 12 is on the second floor. You climb the stairs silently and spread out in the rancid-smelling hallway. The door you want is right ahead of you.

If a teammember assenses the area, read the following.

Room 12 is empty. Wherever Crunch the troll has decided to hang out, it sure isn't here.

If the team bursts into the room, read the following.

The door flies open and you follow it in, gun muzzles tracking around the room.

Which is empty. Not a thing moves, and your entrance was dramatic enough to attract the attention of a corpse.

When the runners examine the room, read the following.

The decor of the room is just…weird. The furniture you'd expect in a low-rent hotel—metal-frame bed, formica table, rickety chair—is all here. But the cracked plaster walls are covered with a weird collection of posters and photos cut from magazines and screamsheets. In pride of place, facing the door, is a poster showing a cold, aloof human cradling a high-tech sniper rifle in his arms. You recognize the figure at once: it's one of the great simsense anti-heros, "The Sniper." The other pictures are along the same lines: hard men, mercs, and other pros.

The closet contains an interesting assortment of clothes, all size XXL. A military-style armored long coat, a set of army fatigues, and a camo overjacket hang from a rod. Two pairs of combat boots stand in the back corner. You notice right away that all this clothing is second-hand army-surplus stuff.

BEHIND THE SCENES

The team may or may not notice several things here. Any runner doing more than just glancing at the army fatigues will notice that the unit designations and shoulder flashes are not standard issue (in fact, they have been clumsily stapled into place). The patch on the right shoulder is not real. It is a photograph of a mountain lion's head cut from a magazine and glued into place. Runners who make an Intelligence/Perception (4) Test realize that all the unit patches, including the photograph, are from Sioux units. (The cat's head, of course, represents the Sioux Special Forces, the Wildcats.)

Under the pillow on the bed is a cheap pocket secretary. The file directory shows it has been used as a diary (presumably by Crunch). The diary file has no security, so anyone can access it. The early entries are nothing of importance, mainly self-aggrandizing lies and the ramblings of a somewhat bent mind. (Anyone with Psychology Skill can make a Success Test against a Target Number 3 to recognize Crunch as a paranoid schizophrenic with homicidal tendencies and a strong Oedipal complex. Trivia, perhaps, but interesting trivia.) Only the last five entries are of any importance. (See **Crunch's Diary**, below.)

Have all runners make an Intelligence/Perception (6) Test to notice that the bed has been moved. Indentations in the carpet show that the bed used to be against the wall; opposite its present position. If the runners move the bed or look under it, they see a large, dark stain on the threadbare carpet. Runners with Biology Skill (or a skill sufficiently close to it on the Skill Web) may make a Success Test against a Target Number of 3 to identify the stain.

Successes	Results
0	It's a dark stain. It smells bad.
1	It's blood.
2	Lots of blood. More blood than you're going to find in a human body.
3	Yep, it's troll blood.
4+	The troll who spilled it wouldn't be able to walk away.

The team will probably try to unearth data about the name in Crunch's diary, Maureen Westlake. See **Legwork**, p. 61, for the relevant information.

CRUNCH'S DIARY

The following are the last five entries in Crunch's diary. The gamemaster should calculate the date from current adventure time.

Date: [ten days ago]

He came back to see me, the officer, and he explained just how important my part in the plan would be. Vital, he said. Crucial. Still doesn't say what the assignment is, but he says it's important. Frag the Boys, they're nothing. I'm in the Sioux army now.

Date: [six days ago]

I still don't know his name, but he let slip that he's a major in the Sioux Special Forces. Says I'm not to tell anyone or else the Wildcats will kill me. Asked me if I'm a good rifle shot.

Date: [five days ago]

He missed our meeting today. Didn't say why, just didn't show. Busy elsewhere? Or dead? If he's dead, I'll avenge him. It's my duty.

Date: [three days ago]

He's back. It's something about another assignment. Brought me a briefcase. I can't say what was in it, but it's wizzer. Big surprise for anybody I don't like. Asked me what I knew about Maureen Westlake. It's going to be soon.

Date: [yesterday]

It's tomorrow. He still won't tell me what it is, but says that when it's over, the Sioux BTL traffic is mine. He smiles when he says that, and I smile too. When it's done, maybe I'll give him a big surprise. Then I'll be a major in the Wildcats.

DEBUGGING

The (standard) problem that can arise is that the runners fail to pick up any of the evidence in the room. Though the other details are interesting and potentially useful, the only vital clue is Crunch's pocket secretary. If the team does not find it, a surviving member of the Barrelhouse Boys or any other contact from Pueblo-Under can "stumble across" the pocket secretary, figure out who it belonged to, and pass it on to the runners.

The next section, **Straight Shooter**, assumes that the runners have learned about Maureen Westlake and have decided to attend her speech, which takes place near the Carlisle hotel. If the team needs some help figuring out what is happening, a convenient NPC can pass on some of the information from the **Maureen Westlake** section of **Legwork**, p. 61.

If the runners do not make the connection or do not show up at the speech, they will learn through the news media that Maureen Westlake was gunned down by a troll sniper who was subsequently killed by Westlake's bodyguards. Evidence indicates that the troll was associated with the Sioux nation's armed forces. (The successful completion of this part of his plan gives Jesse a +1 bonus to his Threat Rating.)

The runners might think that they have lost Jesse for good, and so are at the end of the adventure. If they check with any of their contacts, however, they have a good chance (Target Number 4) of discovering that "that crazy shaman" is making tracks for Seattle. Go to **My Hometown**, p. 51.

STRAIGHT SHOOTER

TELL IT TO THEM STRAIGHT

You figured that the site of Maureen Westlake's speech would be some kind of park, or at least a paved square or something. Actually, it's just an intersection in the low-rent area of town. (Near the Carlisle. Coincidence?) The streets are blocked off with barricades manned by SecForce soldiers. A stage-and-PA setup is in the middle of the intersection. More SecForce troops are doing crowd control.

And there's quite a crowd to control. Squatters and down-and-outers mix with slightly more affluent types. It looks like the whole neighborhood's come out to hear what Maureen's got to say.

Maureen herself is up there on the platform, looking like she owns it. With no introduction, she launches into her speech. She's an amazing orator; you find it difficult to keep from listening to her. But you have to concentrate on other things. You're here on business.

If a player character assenses the area, read the following.

Your heartbeat slows and you slip out of your body like you are shedding a suit of clothes. Insubstantial, you drift through the area. Nothing seems out of the ordinary.

Without warning, something hurtles out of the sky and strikes your astral body with the impact of a bullet-train.

BEHIND THE SCENES

This is the intersection where Maureen is throwing her party. This part of Pueblo is built low to the ground; the buildings are fewer than eight stories and have flat roofs. The letter A on the map represents Aurora, Jesse John's muscle. She is hunkered down below the cornice of the building, out of sight of anyone on the ground. At her feet is a fully-assembled Ranger Arms SM-3 sniper rifle and a very dead troll (Crunch) dressed in a camo outfit similar to the one in the Carlisle hotel room.

This is the plan. When Maureen has gotten well into her speech, Aurora will drop her with the sniper rifle. Then she will push the body of the troll up so that it is visible over the cornice of the building. No doubt the SecForce guards below will open fire at the "sniper" and the troll's body will stop a few rounds (in addition to the single bullet in the throat that killed the troll sometime earlier). If the troll's body goes over the edge, fine; if it stays on the roof, fine. Either way, Aurora will bug out, leaving the sniper rifle behind. The SecForce will find their sniper—dead—and evidence linking him to the Sioux Special Forces. (To reinforce this link, the unfortunate Crunch has another pocket secretary on his person, which contains a copy of his diary file. See **Heartbreak Hotel**, p. 46, for the contents of this diary.)

That is Jesse's plan. Of course, the team might be able to do something to foul it up. Both Aurora and Jesse (who is already

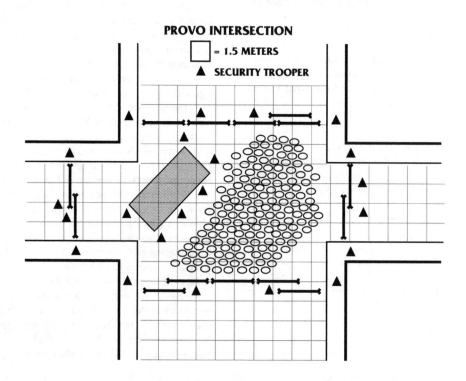

PROVO INTERSECTION

☐ = 1.5 METERS

▲ SECURITY TROOPER

on his way to Seattle) anticipate trouble. Aurora is armed for bear, and Jesse has summoned a Force 6 toxic earth spirit, ordering it to destroy any magicians who try to mess with Aurora. This toxic earth spirit is what jumps any runner going astral in the region. (For details on toxic earth spirits, see **Paranormal Animals of North America**.) As discussed in **The Grimoire**, toxic spirits are summoned in a particular domain (Jesse called his up in a nearby slum), but are free to pursue enemies through other domains. This means a runner cannot dodge Jesse's toxic earth spirit by ducking into a building, which is normally the domain of a hearth spirit. The toxic earth spirit can follow.)

A total 22 Pueblo Security Force troopers are in the area. Their orders are to protect Maureen Westlake at all costs. They are not allowed on the platform with her, but they take their orders very seriously. They will certainly react if a bunch of runners, typically disreputable-looking types kitted out like walking armories, try to talk to Maureen. Their reaction will probably be to keep the "potential troublemakers" under the gun until Maureen is safely out of the area. If the runners try to make a dash for the platform or commit any other potentially hostile act, the SecForce troopers will take them down. The troopers will also be understandably edgy if they see any of the runners flying toward the podium. The runners will have to play this very carefully.

The gamemaster must time things so that the runners arrive just as Maureen starts her speech. Maureen usually talks for about 15 minutes and will do so today—if she lives that long. Aurora will take her shot seven minutes into the speech. (Rolling the dice is a waste of time. If Aurora gets the shot off, it drills Maureen clean between her baby blues, geeking her instantly. Good shooting, Aurora.)

Aurora has a ticket for a flight departing Sea-Tac International Airport the next day in her pocket.

Aurora

A real hardcase supporter of Jesse John, Aurora is a Humanis member. She thinks the policlub's leadership has gone criminally soft. She has thrown her full support behind Jesse's plans to destabilize the NAN. Aurora is a big woman, powerfully built, with short-cropped dark hair and piercing, dark eyes. Aurora is a true believer in the Humanis credo and will fight to the death.

B	Q	S	C	I	W	E	M	R	Armor
5	3	6	2	3	4	0.7	—	3	4/3

Dice Pools: Defense (Armed) 5, Defense (Unarmed) 4, Dodge 3
Skills: Armed Combat 5, Etiquette (Street) 3, Firearms (Rifles) 5, Stealth 3, Unarmed Combat 4
Cyberware: Cybereyes (Low-Light w/flare compensation), Dermal Plating (2), Retractable Spurs, Smartgun Link, Wired Reflexes (2)
Gear: Knife, Ranger Arms SM-3 Sniper Rifle [6 (magazine), 6S2, APDS ammo, with Smartgun Link], Defiance T-250 Shotgun [short-barrel version, 5 (magazine), 3M3], Armor Vest with Plates (4/3)

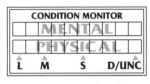

SecForce Trooper (Ten)

He is exceptionally well-trained and dedicated to keeping the peace. He prefers non-violent solutions to any problem, but he is quick to use force—even deadly force—when the occasion warrants.

B	Q	S	C	I	W	E	M	R	Armor
4	3	4	2	3	6	5.5	—	3	6/4

Dice Pools: Defense (Armed) 4, Defense (Unarmed) 3, Dodge 3
Skills: Armed Combat 4, Etiquette (Street) 3, Firearms 4, Police Procedure 3, Stealth 3, Unarmed Combat 3
Cyberware: Smartgun Link
Gear: Ares Predator II [15 (clip), 6M2, with Smartgun Link], Armor Jacket (5/3), Helmet (1/1), Radio

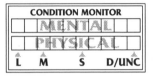

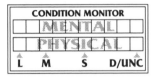

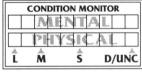

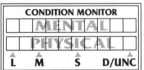

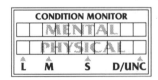

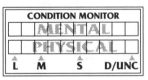

The runners should be ready to head back to Seattle. Go to **My Hometown**, the next section.

DEBUGGING

Several complications can arise out of this encounter. The runners can get themselves geeked, either by Aurora or by the SecForce troopers (if they hose things big-time). If so, too bad: the players should pick up some friends of the original runners and start arranging revenge for their buddies.

If the runners geek Aurora, they can find the airline ticket on her person, leading them to the final confrontation in Seattle. Should they manage to take Aurora alive, they can get even more information out of her through interrogation. (Aurora is a tough nut, but under the right physical and magical persuasion, anyone will crack.) She knows that Jesse has already left for Seattle. She is supposed to join him there when Maureen Westlake is flatlined. She is not sure exactly where Jesse is going, just that she is supposed to take a room at the Council Island Inn and wait for Jesse to contact her. Jesse has not filled her in on his ultimate plan, but she suspects he intends to disrupt a Council meeting. She knows that he has acquired what might be a new kind of bomb from Renraku, but she does not know any details. She can, however, give the player characters the entire rundown on the Ute operation, from the initial setup of Crunch to his murder in his hotel room.

Unless the runners stop her, Aurora will assassinate Maureen Westlake and leave Crunch to take the fall. The evidence planted on Crunch and the drek in his hotel room all point directly to Sioux Special Force involvement in the assassination. The BTL trade is already a sore point between Pueblo and Sioux. (As discussed in the source material, the Pueblo government feels that the Sioux government is not doing enough to crack down on BTL traffickers, and may even

believe that the Sioux government is somehow involved in the trade.) This incident will whip up hatred against the Sioux nation and turn already-chilly diplomatic relations into a veritable cold war. Because this breakup is Jesse's goal, this turn of events will give the Toxic shaman a +1 bonus to his Threat Rating.

If the SecForce troopers find Aurora, dead or alive, at the scene—whether or not Westlake takes a round to the headbone—things will be less clear-cut. The SecForce will conclude that the assassination was a setup of some kind, but will not know who orchestrated it. If it looks as though the SecForce will take Aurora alive, the toxic earth spirit summoned by Jesse (if it is still operational) will kill her to keep her from spilling her guts. With this turn of events, the anti-Sioux faction in Pueblo will still suspect that the Sioux nation was behind the assassination (attempt), but they will have no proof. Relations between the two nations will be slightly cooler for a week or two, but will soon return to normal.

If the runners are caught by SecForce, they should receive one chance to escape from the arresting officers and one chance to persuade the troopers that they were actually trying to stop the assassination. If they fail both these attempts, off they go to jail. Escape should still be possible, albeit much more difficult.

If the runners are unable to interrogate Aurora, they will not find the airline ticket that would send them back to Seattle. If this is the case, the runners may believe that they have lost Jesse and reached the end of the adventure. If they check with any of their newfound contacts, however, they have a good chance (Target Number of 4) of discovering that "that crazy shaman" is heading back to Seattle. The team must make their own way back to the Northwest. Go to **My Hometown**, the next section.

MY HOMETOWN

TELL IT TO THEM STRAIGHT

The city never looked so good. Seattle might be a gray, dirty, bloody, soul-sick town…but it's your gray, dirty, bloody, soul-sick town. As you drink in the familiar landmarks, you start planning your next move.

BEHIND THE SCENES

Once back in Seattle, the runners will have to work their contacts to track down Jesse. (Even if they got the name of the Council Island Inn from Aurora, they should want additional information before jumping into the middle of things again.) The gamemaster should provide the following information to the player characters depending on the direction of the team's inquiries.

JESSE'S ARRIVAL IN SEATTLE

Target Number	Information Available
3	Neither Jesse John nor Ben Johnson (Jesse's previous alias) flew into Seattle over the last two weeks.
5	A man matching Jesse's description flew into Sea-Tac a day or so ago, but his name on the passenger manifest was Denny Sam.

JESSE'S ACCOMMODATIONS

Target Number	Information Available·
5	None of the major hotels in Seattle has reservations for Jesse John or Ben Johnson.
5	The Council Island Inn has a three-day reservation for a Mr. Denny Sam, confirmed by credstick transaction and held safe from cancellation. (Mr. Sam will never show up.)

If the team starts asking around to find out if anything of interest will be happening at Council Island over the next few days, see **Legwork**, p. 62.

Should the team decide to investigate the upcoming Council meeting, guessing (correctly) that Jesse will also be there, go to **Hysteria**, the next section.

DEBUGGING

If the runners are getting skunked, or if they are simply not asking the right questions, their erstwhile employer Karl Brackhaven can get back into the act. The team receives the following message:

Our agreement is still in force. Therefore, I pass on to you some information I received through sources. Our mutual friend's target is the S-S Council meeting tomorrow. You will, no doubt, understand the importance and sensitivity of this matter. I trust you will discharge your obligation, both to me and to your nation.
—KB

How this message arrives will depend on the team's actions. It could show up on an electronic mail "in-basket" or a voice-mail device belonging to one of the runners, or could be delivered by a bonded courier. This note should jack the runners up to find out why the upcoming Council meeting is so important and sensitive.

If the team will not take the hint and go to Council Island, a day later they hear that the Council meeting ended in general mayhem. Representatives of several tribes got into a screaming match and some Council members even exchanged blows. The Council is now dangerously unstable, with a very real chance that the Salish-Shidhe nation will disintegrate. The disintegration of the Council would bring only bad things to Seattle. (This is exactly what Jesse John wanted to accomplish. He has succeeded in the third part of his destabilizing plan and gains a +1 bonus to his Threat Rating. He immediately leaves Seattle, presumably to pursue additional phases of his twisted plan. The team will not be able to get a line on him, and so they have lost. Go to **Picking Up the Pieces**, p. 56.)

The runners may attempt to get help either from Lone Star or the FBI. This is a bad idea, and may well get the team arrested. The FBI still consider the runners' names mud, especially if any Feds have been geeked. This information has been passed on to Lone Star. Should the runners make phone contact with either Lone Star or the Feds, they will be invited to come in and make their appeal in person. Of course, this is simply an invitation to a trap. If the runners are dumb enough to fall for it, bag 'em, lock 'em up, and forget about 'em.

If they try to communicate their suspicions to the Salish-Shidhe Council, they get much the same reaction. The runners' names are mud here, too, but the Council security forces will not try to arrest them; they will simply hang up on them or kick them out, then promptly forget they ever existed.

HYSTERIA

TELL IT TO THEM STRAIGHT

Okay, chummer, this is the big one.

BEHIND THE SCENES

GETTING ONTO THE ISLAND

If the runners want to attend the Council meeting, the first order of business is to get onto Council Island. This is not particularly easy (pp. 59-62, **Seattle Sourcebook**). It is tribal land, and so visitors need to jump through the same bureaucratic hoops required to enter the Salish-Shidhe nation proper. The red tape is discussed in the sourcebook chapter on the Salish-Shidhe nation under **Laws**.

Access to the island is via ferries or along I-90. The ferry docks and the road accesses to the island are well-guarded. The security detachments comprise ten Council Island Police (use the **Street Cop** archetype, p. 171, **SR**, but arm them with HK227 SMGs and Full Heavy Armor) and eight Metroplex Guards (use the **Mercenary** archetype, p. 40, **SR**, but arm them with AK-98s). Heavy firepower is provided by six Salish-Shidhe Rangers and two Ranger Combat Mages (see the stats in **On the Border**, p. 18). One of the Rangers carries an Enfield AS7 assault shotgun (for riot control), and a Panther Assault Cannon is bipod-mounted behind sandbags. Air cover is provided by four Yellowjacket rotorcraft each packing two light machine guns on hardpoints, and anti-air defense comes from four SAM teams (using the man-portable SAMs on p. 59 of the **Street Samurai Catalog**) dispersed around the island.

Gamemaster's Note: The preceding details are provided just to let the runners know that they are playing in the big leagues now, not because all this hardware is going to be used. If the team starts any unpleasantness, hose them down good. They deserve it.

Every potential visitor's credstick is checked for the appropriate paperwork, and the visitor's person is scanned. The gamemaster should make a 9-dice Perception Test against the Concealability of any weapon the players are carrying to see whether the sensor picks it up. If so, the visitor is politely turned away.

Cyberarms present a special problem. The security detachment offers any runner with obvious cyberwear two options: leave quietly or else have the cyberlimb disabled for the duration of his stay on Council Island. Disabling the limb takes one minute and does not permanently damage the device. Re-enabling the limb requires a Biotech (B/R) Success Test against a Target Number of 4. If the runner leaves the island in an ordinary manner, any security officer can re-enable the limb without need for a Success Test.

Visitors who do not have the appropriate paperwork, who are packing weapons, or who refuse to have any obvious cyberarms disabled are not allowed to enter Council Island.

GRAND COUNCIL LODGE

The Council meeting takes place in the Grand Council Lodge. The route between the point at which the team entered the island and the Grand Council Lodge is lined with enough Council Island Police, Rangers, and combat mages to reduce the runners to catfood without breaking a sweat. ("One catfood-worth" is a standard troop size in the Council Lodge.)

The Grand Council Lodge is a huge building, apparently wooden, and in the style of a Northwest Indian longhouse, but on a much larger scale. The longhouse illusion ends at the door, however. Inside, it is laid out much like any major corporate building. The high-ceilinged lobby, decorated with local native art, is packed with almost two catfood-worth of troops, while another catfood-worth patrols the hallways.

The council chamber is dominated by a huge circular table around which the tribal representatives sit. No provisions are made for spectators on this floor. When the Lodge was built, the architect anticipated the possibility of open sessions, and so the council chamber features a large spectator gallery one floor up. The architect made a mistake in the layout of the building, however. The only access to the second floor is a somewhat narrow stairway. Everyone going to this floor, council members and visitors alike, has to use the stairway. Security funnels everyone to this access-point and tries to manage crowd control and security checks from their vantage point on the stairs.

The staircase is covered by only two guards (each dot on the map represents one fully armed and somewhat edgy Ranger). This is where the team can make their move to lose security and get free access to the rest of the second floor. The stairway can accommodate only 30 people (not including the Rangers). When the team climbs the stairs, the balance of the crowd is made up of normal visitors (use the **Pedestrian**, p. 116, **SS**; these guys are just extras). At the top of the staircase, the door leading into the gallery is open, but it can be closed and locked quickly. The other doors, leading to the service rooms shown on the map, are locked with simple mechanical locks. Creative player characters should have little difficulty arranging a diversion to get themselves into the service rooms for a quick, unobserved look-see…at least for a while.

If the Rangers become aware that a group has broken free from the herd of visitors, a team of four Rangers and one combat mage is dispatched to round them up. How close this team is on the runners' heels depends on how our heroes orchestrated their initial getaway, but the Rangers will be at least three turns behind. Two other individuals are tagging along with the Ranger squad, both invisible. One is a Renraku Field Op combat mage (use stats from **The Chase**, p. 27). The other is Agent Della Cooper. The Ranger squad will stay together. The Renraku mage and the agent, both unaware of the other's presence, split off from the squad. Another ranger squad of the same composition will enter the fray in 20 turns, and a third in another 20 turns.

GRAND COUNCIL LODGE MAP KEY

Corridors 1–4

These corridors lead to sections of the Grand Council Lodge not relevant to this adventure. The doors are secured with complex maglocks. The gamemaster should manipulate the team heartlessly to prevent them from using any of these corridors (they cannot pick the locks, pursuit is on their heels, and so on).

Meeting Rooms

The three meeting rooms are set up like comfortable corporate boardrooms. They are designed for private discussions, briefings, and so on. Plaques on the doors identify them as "Meeting Room 1," "Meeting Room 2," and "Meeting Room 3."

Telecom Room

The phone-switching equipment for this floor is located in this room. The door is secured with a simple maglock. A panel on the door reads "Telecom Room—Authorized Personnel Only."

Storage Room

This room contains vacuums, brooms, and other cleaning supplies. The door is unlocked and has no sign on it.

HVAC Control Room

The computers that control the Lodge's heating, ventilation, and air conditioning equipment are located in this room. Several large air ducts run overhead here. This is where Jesse is hiding. The door is secured with a simple maglock. A panel on the door reads "HVAC Control Room—Authorized Personnel Only."

Gamemaster's Note: All the rest of the space around the gallery is taken up by rooms that cannot be accessed from this corridor network.

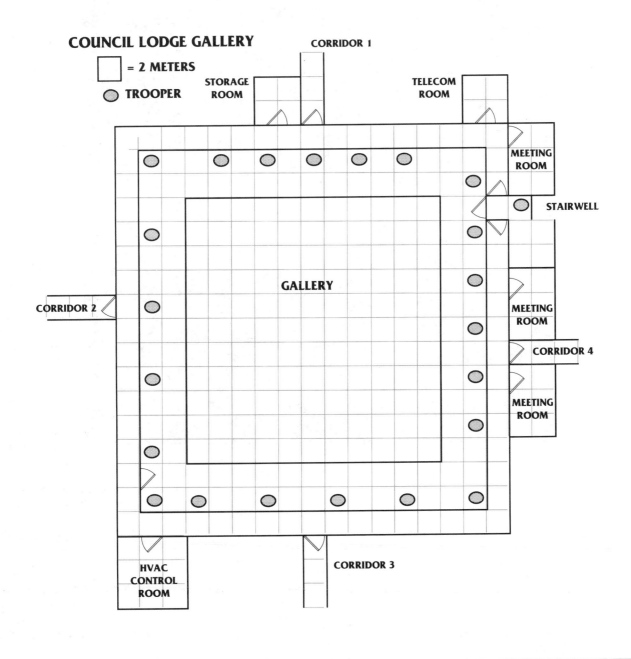

COUNCIL LODGE GALLERY

☐ = 2 METERS

⬭ TROOPER

CORRIDOR 1

STORAGE ROOM

TELECOM ROOM

MEETING ROOM

STAIRWELL

GALLERY

CORRIDOR 2

MEETING ROOM

CORRIDOR 4

MEETING ROOM

HVAC CONTROL ROOM

CORRIDOR 3

GAMEMASTERING THE PURSUIT

This scenario should result in a tense, exciting chase, leading to a climactic battle with Jesse John. The Renraku combat mage and Agent Cooper can be used as tools toward this end. For example, if the runners decide to ambush and geek the Ranger squad—difficult, but possible—the mage and the Fed can complicate matters, either now or later. (As it turns out, geeking the squad is not a good plan. The runners might need the fire support when they meet Jesse.)

It is important to understand the motives of the various groups and to keep them in mind while running this scenario (not an easy task). The Ranger squad simply wants to eliminate a possible assassination attempt against the Council members in the chamber below. They will do whatever is necessary to achieve that goal. The Renraku mage has orders to retrieve the missing tonal generator, but to stay alive in the process. Agent Cooper has her heart set on executing the "Humanis scum" who played her and her boss for fools earlier in the adventure. The mage and the Fed will ignore each other unless their goals come into conflict. Neither feels any hostility toward the Rangers. The Rangers, on the other hand, are in a shoot-first-and-frag-the-questions mood, and will take down the mage and Fed if they spot them.

FINDING JESSE

If a player character takes the time to assense the area, Jesse's psychic spoor is easy to detect. It leads directly from the stairway to the HVAC (Heating/Ventilation/Air Conditioning) Control Room.

The Council meeting is scheduled to begin at noon. At exactly 11:55, Jesse triggers his tonal generator. He has installed the device in a major air duct so that its sound will be broadcast to all parts of the building. The tonal generator's sound comprises both high and low harmonics, well out of the range of normal (meta)human hearing. Only characters with cyberears and high- or low-frequency response will hear it. They will notice an aggravating buzz in the appropriate range(s). Cyberear-equipped characters who take one turn to concentrate on the sound can determine that it is coming through the ventilation system (which may give them a clue to Jesse's location).

TONAL GENERATOR

The tonal generator has the following effects on all (meta)humans who can hear its tone. It increases all emotional responses, particularly negative ones such as anger. While the generator is operating, everyone in its range is touchier. Usually calm people become edgy; normally excitable people now have hair-trigger tempers, and anyone involved in an emotionally charged situation is likely to fly into a sudden uncontrollable rage. The generator will also make the Ranger squad more likely to open fire at the slightest provocation. The players should be informed about the emotional changes their characters are feeling and encouraged to roleplay these changes.

In addition, the tonal generator makes concentration on any task much more difficult. All Target Numbers increase by 1 while the generator is operating.

Characters can try to counter the effects of the tonal generator. A white-noise generator has a chance of neutralizing the tonal generator's effects. Roll a number of dice equal to the white-noise generator's rating against a Target Number of 6. One success eliminates the increase to Target Numbers; two or more successes eliminate the emotional effects for everyone within range of the white-noise generator. Blocking the ears or using damping on cyberears is only partially effective, since the tonal generator's harmonics reverberate in the skull bones. Each turn, any character attempting to block or dampen the tonal generator's effects should make a Willpower (8) Test. One success eliminates the increase to Target Numbers for that turn; two or more successes eliminate the emotional effects for that turn. The only way to completely eliminate the effects of the tonal generator is to deactivate it. Luckily, this is very easy because it has a clearly marked On/Off switch.

THE FINAL CONFLICT

Jesse has come into this situation prepared. He is accompanied by two Rating 6 Toxic Water Spirits and one Rating 6 Toxic Earth Spirit. He is holed up in the HVAC Control Room behind a locked door, but is using a clairvoyance spell to watch the hallways around him. As soon as he senses the runners and the Rangers, he sends the toxic earth spirit to start the festivities. The spirit is ordered to destroy the Rangers. Jesse wants to save the runners for himself.

Remember, Jesse is very intelligent, even if he is quite insane, and he will make the best possible use of his impressive armory of spells. The two Rating 6 Toxic Water Spirits will help him, and he can also draw on his Threat Rating. Jesse is a nasty individual, perhaps too nasty for the team to handle alone.

DEBUGGING

This is where the Ranger squad, the Renraku mage, and Agent Cooper can figure into the equation. If it looks like the team is going to get its collective butt handed to it—and if the gamemaster feels charitable—a few surviving Rangers can get in on the action (they somehow managed to defeat the toxic earth spirit). If, on the other hand, the team looks as though it is heading for a romp-and-stomp on Jesse, the toxic earth spirit, gorged on Rangers, should come looking for dessert. The mage and Agent Cooper can be thrown in as wild cards on either side of the battle. For a really spectacular finish, try for the best of both worlds: the Rangers show up at ground zero but with the toxic earth spirit in hot pursuit. Remember that the only weapons the team will have are those they could sneak by the Council Island security forces. (Lightly armed runners with deactivated cyberlimbs versus an angry Toxic shaman? Nobody ever said this was going to be easy, chummer.)

The gamemaster should conclude this adventure as he or she sees fit. The Rangers and Agent Cooper will quickly recognize that the runners were fighting against Jesse John and that the team had no chance to plant the tonal generator. The obvious conclusion is that Jesse planted the device and the team was trying to block his plans—whatever they were. A Ranger shaman who knows Analyze Truth is readily available, and will verify the runners' story. Unless the team has geeked an inordinate number of Rangers and other security personnel, the Salish-Shidhe will be glad just to see the last of the runners and will escort them off Council Island with a stern injunction never to return. Agent Cooper's actions will depend on how many Federal agents got themselves messily dead as a result of the runners' actions. If the body count is minimal, she will let them go…but will keep a close eye on them in the future. If the morgue is full, she will make every effort to arrest them.

And what about the tonal generator? If the Renraku mage has not been forced to reveal himself, he will try to snatch it and make his escape from the Lodge. If the runners decide to keep it, Renraku will make increasingly determined attempts to get it back. If the team wants to regain some semblance of a normal life, the best thing to do might be to hand the device back to Renraku and forget the whole thing. (But what nastiness would Renraku get up to with a functioning tonal generator?)

The team is free to take whatever action they feel appropriate with regard to Karl Brackhaven. As promised, he will contact the team and pay off his debt if their mission was successful. Any attempts to extract physical retribution for his deception will be difficult, because he is always surrounded by heavy guard.

Future relations between the team and the Feds depend, again, on the number of body bags bearing FBI crests. Both Drummond and Cooper can develop into contacts, acquaintances, or nemeses.

IF THE TEAM FAILS

If the team fails to deactivate the tonal generator, the meeting in the council chamber takes place as planned…and begins to resemble an Urban Brawl game. Several representatives get into fistfights, others storm out, most scream themselves hoarse. Relationships between the tribes have never been so strained, and the Salish-Shidhe Council appears to be on the verge of breaking up.

Jesse has accomplished his goal. If he managed to escape with his life, his Threat Rating gains another +1 bonus. He immediately leaves Seattle, perhaps to pursue another phase in his nefarious schemes. The runners—if any have survived—or their friends and heirs may try to track him down. Only the gamemaster knows whether they will succeed.

PICKING UP THE PIECES

Depending on how the team handled themselves throughout the adventure, they may have as undying enemies any or all of the following groups: the FBI, the Humanis Policlub, Renraku, the Salish-Shidhe Rangers, the Council Island Police, the Pueblo Security Force, and the Ute Security Force. (It has been a busy few days.) If Jesse managed to escape, it is quite likely that he, too, will come gunning for the runners some time in the future—once he has become even more powerful, of course.

The political situation in the NAN depends on how successful the runners were. If they failed to prevent the run on the Pueblo Net, then Sioux and Pueblo will be on the outs. If they failed to keep Maureen Westlake alive, Ute will hate Sioux. If they were not able to disarm the tonal generator before the Council meeting degenerated into a free-for-all, the entire Salish-Shidhe Council will be highly unstable. No matter how bad things appear at the moment, however, everyone will pull back from the edge. Despite the doom predicted by its detractors, the NAN works.

Political pressure and diplomatic guidance from other NAN nations will bring the feuding countries back together again—not immediately and not without heated words—but eventually the wounds will heal. The NAN may well emerge from this stronger than ever. (Jesse's world view was too narrow for him to see just how difficult it would be to destroy a complex federation like the NAN.) The current situation should be concealed from the runners for awhile. Play up the instabilities around the continent and allow everyone to believe that the whole situation is going to turn into a massive bloodbath. (A little uncertainty makes the team's life more interesting.) Future runs might develop from the effects of various groups grabbing for the advantages to be gained from the widespread confusion and fear.

AWARDING KARMA

Apart from Karl Brackhaven's payment, which the team may refuse when they learn his true identity, there is little chance for monetary gain in this adventure. This is balanced by a potential Karma windfall, however. Award team Karma as follows:

The decker Ram in Pueblo is killed or dumped	2
Maureen Westlake escapes assassination	2
The tonal generator is deactivated	2
Renraku does not regain the tonal generator	1
Jesse John is killed or captured	2
Aurora is killed or captured	1
Special Agent Drummond is killed	-1
Joey (the young ork) is killed	-2

The gamemaster should also award individual Karma points according to the guidelines on page 160 of the **Shadowrun** rules.

▼ ▼ ▼ ▼ ▼ ▼ ▼ ▼

LEGWORK

To follow up on or obtain clues in this adventure, the player characters need to investigate the people, places, and situations involved. The best way for runners to get the information they need is through contacts. This section provides Success Tables containing information the runners may be able to get from their sources.

A Success Test using Street or Corporate Etiquette, Target Number 4, typically serves to find out what a contact does or does not know. The amount of information available depends on the number of successes achieved. Adventurers who succeed more than once gain all the information available to all previous levels of success.

The gamemaster should not limit the player character's interaction with his contact to a few simple, abstract die rolls. The meeting should be played out in full: contacts are characters with their own lives, points of view, and needs, not simply spigots of information to be turned on and off automatically.

The player character should roll the dice equal to his Etiquette Skill to determine what information the contact knows and is willing to impart. Once the player character's number of successes has been determined, the meeting can take place. The gamemaster can play the encounter with the appropriate information level in mind. Meetings should be tailored to the "personality" of specific contacts. Some will want to have a straightforward meet in a specific type of place, others will have more elaborate forms of information exchange set up.

Contacts are generally considered trustworthy, as long as the runners play it safe. A player character should never compromise his contact by making it obvious that information came from him, or by revealing that the team may be planning to hit some group with which the contact is affiliated. Are the contact's ties stronger to his group or to the runner? A good runner never tests those ties by putting his contact in a situation where he must choose.

Keep in mind when setting up a meet whether or not the runner has to pay for his contact's services, and how long it will be before the contact may want information or a favor in return. Remember, most streets are two-way.

The information below is presented in the order the player characters are likely to encounter it.

KARL BRACKHAVEN

The only way the runners can track down information on Brackhaven is if they have somehow acquired a photograph of him (perhaps through a cybereye camera?).

Appropriate Contacts (Target 6)

Any Street Contact, Media Producer, Metahuman Rights Activist

Successes	Result
0	"Never seen the bleeder before in my life. Some kinda corporator, huh?"
1	"Karl…something. Blockhouse, Brackhaus …Brackhaven, yeah. What are you doing running around with Humanis scum, eh, chummer?"
2–3	"Yeah, right. Central Seattle chapter, Humanis Policlub. He's the prez."
4	"They say he's a moderate…whatever that means for a Humanis type."
5+	"The way I hear it, there's a schism in the policlub. The lunatic fringe think Brackhaven's too soft. They're striking out on their own."

HUMANIS POLICLUB

The following information on Brackhaven is available if the runners have a direct contact with the Humanis Policlub.

Appropriate Contacts (Target 5)

Any Humanis Policlub Member

Successes	Result
0	"Whatchu doin' wif a pitcher a' Mr. Brackhaven, elf-lover?"
1–2	"Yeah, Karl Brackhaven. Central Seattle chapter prez. A righteous guy. Right-thinking."
3	"He's going soft—lost his cojones. Time for a change, you ask me."
4–5	"Yeah, well, I think Brackhaven's all right. But there's this real hard-line group, they're making a move behind his back."
6+	"The lunatic fringe, they've got some real brain-fried plan going down. I think Brackhaven wants to stop it."

JESSE JOHN

Jesse is bad news; even the people who agree with his harebrained schemes would make that assessment. His native descent does not prevent him from hating everything the Native American Nations stands for—and he is going to do something about it. Jesse John is a shaman of considerable power, but there is something twisted inside him…

Appropriate Contacts (Target Number 6)

Fetishmonger, Street Shaman, any Tribal Contact

Successes	Result
0	"Jesse John? Oh yeah, that crazy Indian."
1	"Don't ask me how or why, but he's in with those Humanis slots."
2–3	"Huh. An Indian who hates Indians—with a vengeance. Go figure."
4–5	"He split with the Humanis leadership over policy, I guess. Thinks they're too moderate. Right."
6+	"Guy's a real drek-hot shaman, but he's real twisted, too. Toxic. Get my drift?"

HUMANIS POLICLUB

The following information on Jesse John is available if the runners have a direct contact with the Humanis Policlub.

Appropriate Contacts (Target 5)

Any Humanis Policlub member

Successes	Result
0	"An Indian? In the Humanis Policlub? You're kidding, right?"
1	"Jesse? Yeah, I met him. He's an 'oreo': dark on the outside, white on the inside, you know?"
2–3	"Had some kinda way-out plan, don't know exactly what. Brackhaven squelched him. Haven't seen Jesse lately, now that you mention it…"
4	"I think he quit the policlub, took some of the other nutters with him."
5+	"The prez is trying to stop Jesse, whatever he's doing."

THE FBI

The UCAS Federal Bureau of Investigation has learned that the runners have been hired by Karl Brackhaven, and so must be working for the Humanis Policlub. Because the Bureau also thinks that Jesse John is running his operation with the blessings of the policlub, they have reached the understandable (but mistaken) conclusion that the runners are operating as back-up for Jesse.

Appropriate Contacts (Target Number 6)

Any Street or Law Enforcement Contact

Successes	Result
0	"Nah, they're lying low. Word on the street says the FBI Anti-Gang Squad tried to lean on the Ancients. Now the Feds are keeping busy attending memorial services. Har, har, har…"
1–2	"Feds, huh? Yeah, well…you didn't hear it from me, but they're putting the heat on the Humanis Policlub. The Humanis freaks are into something real heavy and the Bureau's out to get 'em."
3–4	"You're asking me about the Feds? Chummer, they're not after me so what do I care….How come you're in bed with those Humanis drek-heads, anyway?"
5+	"Oh yeah, the Feds are on your case. Bad news? You ain't heard the half of it. Fragging Drummond is leading the team."

SPECIAL AGENT CLIVE DRUMMOND

Drummond's reputation as a straight-arrow terrorist-buster is not just Bureau legend. On the street, his rep has taken on almost mythic proportions. Drummond is the great equalizer: if you are working on the side of the angels, he will give you a fair shake. If you are on the other side of the line, all he will give you is a 9mm migraine.

Appropriate Contacts (Target Number 6)

Any Street or Law Enforcement Contact

Successes	Result
0	"Drummond? JAFF, chummer. Just Another Fragging Fed."
1	"Hoo-boy. You got Drummond after you? What did you do, hold the Space Needle for ransom?"
2	"Drummond's one of the best, boyo. If he's after you, he'll get you, sooner or later. He is leading his very own anti-terrorist squad, and he's a hermetic mage. That makes things plenty hot enough."
3	"I hate to tell you this, chummer, but you are well and truly under the gun. If Drummond gets you, he'll put you on ice until he can check your story. And the way I hear it, his version is the right one: you're working for the Humanis Policlub. How the frag can you look in a mirror?"
4+	"He's got this assistant, Cooper I think it is. She is a tough bitch; has this thing against Humanis members and tends to geek on sight. Which is like breathing for her. She's a better mage than Drummond and she's got a sharper street edge, too."

▼ ▼ ▼ ▼ ▼ ▼ ▼

AGENT DELLA COOPER

Agent Cooper has almost as big a rep on the street as Drummond. Unfortunately, hers is not anywhere near as clean. Her attitude toward the Humanis Policlub is well known. When Humanis members are involved in one of her investigations her approach is said to be "shoot first and make up the answers to any questions later."

Appropriate Contacts (Target Number 6)

Any Street or Law Enforcement Contact

Successes	Result
0	"Della Cooper? Yeah, she's Drummond's trained monkey."
1	"Real kick-butt type. She's a regular Fed, but she's got a big attitude. Read me?"
2	"Chummer, Agent Cooper doesn't know you, but she already hates you anyway. You even talk to the Humanis Policlub and she has a slug with your name on it. She's a real steady hand, if you know what I mean."
3	"Good shot, bad attitude, great bod, wicked temper. They call her the Angel of Death. I think she's also a mage, to top it all off."
4+	"Word is her lover was geeked by some Humanis scum a while back. Which would go a long way toward explaining the attitude. If what I hear about your employer is true, she is not going to be looking to negotiate with you."

RAM

Ram is the street name of a decker-for-hire who works out of Denver. When he was younger, he spent a lot of time running naked in the Matrix. A few close encounters with nasty forms of IC gave him brain damage, however. While his intellect and abilities are still as sharp as ever, he is now a true sociopath: he believes his is the only life that matters, that the pain and death of others is inconsequential, and that he is completely justified in taking whatever steps are needed to get what he wants. His consummate skill with his Fairlight deck is unquestioned.

Appropriate Contacts (Target Number 7)

Any Street Contact (if the contact is a Decker, the Target Number drops to 4)

Successes	Result
0	"Ram? Sounds like a decker name, but I don't know him."
1	"Real hot hired talent. He's the best with a Fairlight you're ever going to see. He comes off a bit high-strung, though. Hear he's just landed a new job, something for an out-of-towner. I think it's Jesse something."
2	"Ram's a hard bastard. He was shacking up with this joygirl, but he geeked her for using his razor. "
3–4	"Lots of young deckers want to be like Ram. You know he used to run the Pueblo Net naked? I tell 'em they're crazy. I mean, look at him: personality-blasted, just as likely to kill you as look at you. In fact, he's more likely to kill you if you look at him first. Role model? Him? Like drek."
5	"Hey, small world. Just ran into Ram an hour ago. Says he's doing a one-off for a guy called Jesse, running something heavy with the Net. I don't envy him."
6+	"I hear he's got a real edge on this one. Some guy—John something?—met him down at the Kokomo and gave him a data key that's going to let him bypass the ice."

THE PUEBLO "NET"

Though hooked up to the rest of the Matrix, the computer system serving the Pueblo Corporate Council is unique enough to warrant its own name. People call it the Net (and the N is audibly capitalized). Every feature of the Pueblo Net is half a decade more sophisticated than anything else in the Matrix, and it shows. The IC is tougher, the architecture more efficient, the algorithms more elegant...cruising the Net is an aesthetic dream for a decker—if he or she survives it.

Appropriate Contacts (Target Number 10)

Any Street or Corporate Contact (if the contact is a Decker, the Target Number drops to 3)

Successes	Result
0	"'The Net, that's what the deckers call this corner of the Matrix. And it's tough, chummer, you'd better believe it."
1–2	"Yeah, I tried to bust into the Net once. I hit the first SAN and thought I'd cracked the ice nice and quiet. I was expecting a log-on message—you know, something user-friendly. You know what I got? 'All hope abandon, ye who enter here...' and that's as far as it got before I was punching ESCAPE so hard I sprained a fragging finger. Man, it knew I was a decker, and it knew I didn't belong. That's the Net."
3	"Sophisticated drek, chummer. What's standard ice where you come from? White, maybe gray? Black only if you're playing with the big boys? Surpriiise! Black's the norm here, with some real nasty twists. There's a kind of black IC that calls in ice from other nodes. Wiz, huh? We call it 'party ice'."
4+	"The fragging architecture itself changes, man. Adaptive parallelism at its finest, self-programming hardware. We call them SPASICs—Self-Programmable Application-Specific Integrated Circuits. Wiz like you wouldn't believe...in theory. In practice, you come prancing into a node and meet up with some party ice, so you try to prance out again. But the dataline you came in on is gone, or it leads somewhere else—maybe somewhere worse."

PUEBLO-UNDER

This is the name given to an extensive network of tunnels beneath the city of Pueblo. Many of these tunnels were excavated for sewers and storm drains during the 20th century, but were closed off as civil engineering technology improved. These tunnels now provide a warm, dry home for a tribe of orks and trolls who call themselves the Underground Awakened.

Appropriate Contacts (Target Number 6)

Any Street Contact

Successes	Result
0	"Pueblo-what? Whoa, chummer, you've been listening to too many wild rumors. Ain't nothin' under Pueblo."
1	"Well, I've heard about it, but I don't know too much. It's some kind of tunnel complex. Don't know what lives down there and don't wanna know."
2	"I've seen some old city plans—I'm talking pre-computer here, real hard-copy maps—and man, would you be blown away to see what's under the city. Couple hundred klicks of tunnels, lifting stations, pump houses, you name it. Most aren't used any more. What a wizzer place to vanish, eh?"
3	"'There's already people down there. Orks, trolls—your generic trogs. Call themselves the Underground Awakened..."
4+	"Sometimes I think those guys have got it together better than we do up here. Some of our tribes have lost dignity. The Underground Awakened may be closer to the old ways than we are."

THE UNDERGROUND AWAKENED

After the Awakening, many goblinized tribe members found it impossible to stay in their former tribal groups. Many of those who became elves moved away from the cities and founded elven subtribes. The majority of orks and trolls, however, moved to or remained in the city—tribeless "lost ones." Some orks and trolls, however, banded together and formed their own tribal group, the Underground Awakened. They took up residence in Pueblo-Under, a large network of tunnels beneath the city of Pueblo. Here, in conditions that suited their newly-changed bodies, they built up a strong and stable tribe, proudly following the old ways as closely as possible. Though many still miss the tribes into which they were born and from which their changed bodies wrenched them, the Underground Awakened have a strong sense of tribal kinship.

Appropriate Contacts (Target Number 8)

Any Street, Law Enforcement, or Tribal Contact (Law Enforcement contacts have a Target Number of 6)

Successes	Result
0	"Sorry, chummer. Sounds to me like the kind of name a group of orks would take, but I don't know anything about a specific group."
1	"Oh, them. Yeah, buncha trogs livin' in the sewers. House beautiful, huh?"
2	"They call themselves a tribe. They're actually more like an organized crime family. Mainly they're into BTLs…"
3	"…at least, that's what the rumors say. But the rumors are wrong. Okay, there's a couple of rotten apples running BTLs, but the Underground Awakened tribal council is trying to stamp it out."
4+	"Mary Hawkmoon is the chief of the Underground Awakened. (Yeah, a female. I think these guys have kept the traditions that suit them and tubed the rest.) She's the daughter of an influential Ute subchief, but she had to leave when she Awakened as a troll. Rough luck, huh? But she's a good sort, strongminded and honest."

MAUREEN WESTLAKE

Maureen Westlake is a mundane, but she possesses a great deal of political power. Middle-aged, she has the energy level of someone half her age and uses it to great effect in her personal war against governmental corruption and the BTL trade. Her current tactic is to build opposition within the community itself against the BTL traffickers. "If the people of a neighborhood resist," she often says, "there can be no BTL business in that neighborhood. Never underestimate the power of the people."

Maureen has become a focus for everyone who opposes the organized BTL trade. Her actions cause problems for the BTL czars, but she is safe from retribution: they know that she would do them even more damage as a martyr.

Appropriate Contacts (Target Number 4)

Any resident of Pueblo or Pueblo-Under

Successes	Result
0	"Some loudmouth politico. Who cares?"
1	"Maureen? Sure I heard of her, everybody's heard of her. She's dead set on a war against BTL. If you ask me, she's playing with fire. The dealers are going to off her one day."
2	"These days she's doing some kind of traveling road show, making speeches in bad parts of towns. Always pulls in a big crowd, always gets a standing O afterwards. Her next show's going to be somewhere on Center Street, near 4th, I think. Today, tomorrow, some time soon."
3+	"I wouldn't want to be in her bodyguards' shoes. Sure she travels with armed goons, but she won't let them near the stage when she's giving a speech."

ACTIVITY ON COUNCIL ISLAND

The Salish-Shidhe Council normally holds its meetings in Bellingham. Recently, however, some Council members have been lobbying to hold Council meetings in other parts of the nation to demonstrate the Council's good will toward all nations. The next site on the list is Council Island, Seattle. Obviously, a meeting of this importance requires a level of security above and beyond that usually available on the Island. The Council Island Police has requested—and received—help from the Rangers and from the Metroplex Guard. The Seattle meeting is expected to be a hot one as there are several touchy subjects on the agenda.

Appropriate Contacts (Target Number 4)

Any Seattle Contacts (Media, Tribal, or Law Enforcement Contacts have a Target Number of 3)

Successes	Result
0	"What's the meeting about? Same kinda talk-talk they always have. Who cares?"
1	"Something's going on, but I don't know exactly what it is. Security on Council Island is going through the roof. The Metroplex Guard is out in force along with the CIP [Council Island Police], and I've even seen Rangers wandering around looking for someone to shoot."
2	"You brain-dead or what? Sure something's going down. The whole fragging Salish-Shidhe Council is having a special meeting on the Island. And it's not a closed session. If you can get a visitor's pass to Council Island, you can show up. But don't try to get any hardware inside."
3	"Gonna be some show, chummer. You know what's on the agenda? Some of the tribes are going after the Cascade Orks for aiding and abetting illegal panzer runs. The Sinsearach are hopping mad about some uranium mine around Cle Elum—Cascade Orks, again. The Nootka want something done to cut back the industry around Prince George. And UCAS has sent some rep over to bitch about the current policy of shipping dirty cargo through the Port of Seattle. Yeah, gonna be some show."
4+	"Jon Moses is chairing the thing, and you know what? I don't envy him at all. Unless he keeps the lid on tight, tempers are going to flame and the whole thing's going to turn nasty. Real nasty. Like, REAL nasty, you get what I'm saying to you?"

THE TONAL GENERATOR

This is what Jesse John "acquired" from the boys at Renraku. Determining its nature and function requires an Electronics Skill Test. The Target Number is 5 for an intact unit, 10 for the damaged unit from **Kokomo**.

Successes	Result
0	It is an electronic device. (Unfortunately, if the player characters are looking at the damaged unit, it is not much of anything because it recently stopped a piece of high-velocity metal.)
1–2	It is a sound generator of some kind.
3–5	A modulator circuit is attached to the unit that appears to be designed to produce harmonics of any given tone.
6+	You vaguely remember reading somewhere about how certain harmonics affect the emotions.

Repairing the damaged tonal generator requires an Electronics B/R Skill Test and is virtually impossible (Target Number 15). Very little information is available on the tonal generator on the street. It was one of Renraku's top-secret projects. Even the ashes of burned memos are treated with serious security. (How Jesse found out about the thing is a mystery.) The runners will have to really dig to get any information.

Appropriate Contacts (Target Number 10)

Any Corporate Contact (The Target Number is 8 if the runners have a contact within Renraku)

Successes	Result
0	"Tone generator, huh? Doesn't sound like the kind of thing any of the major corps would be into. Sure it isn't a musical instrument?"
1	"Hmmm…I heard something a while back, what was it…? Yeah—Renraku Seattle's got a new department they call 'The Shop.' But I know they also just poached some guy away from MCT, some expert in sonics or something."
2	"You got it, chummer, 'The Shop' at Renraku Seattle. Something to do with the effect of harmonics on animals…"
3	"…and not only animals, if you catch my drift."
4	"Mind control, chummer. Well, more like emotion control. And you didn't hear that from me."
5	"The way I hear it, somebody busted in and made off with their two prototype units. Renraku is drekking mad about it."
6+	"What the frag are you asking me for anyway? According to Renraku, it was you guys who lifted the prototypes."

CAST OF SHADOWS

SPECIAL AGENT CLIVE DRUMMOND

Special Agent Drummond is a legend in the FBI. An expert in counterterrorism, he has defused more potentially explosive situations than anyone can count, usually with surprisingly little bloodshed. Occasionally, circumstances dictate that the terrorists be completely wiped out. Drummond has shown himself equal to that challenge, also. Drummond looks like anything but a terrorist-smashing legend. He is middle-aged, balding, and looks soft around the edges. His face is kindly and he usually has a somewhat troubled, perplexed look. When he is not wearing his FBI armor (which he prefers to wear only when a situation may become highly volatile), he seems more like an ineffectual favorite uncle than a trained agent.

He speaks softly when he speaks at all, which is only when he has something really important to say. Drummond is a straight arrow in the truest sense of the word. He is completely incorruptible and demands 100 percent from himself and his team. Though he knows "the book" inside and out, he is smart enough to know when to throw it away. He is a hard man, but eminently fair, usually willing to give a dog the first bite (but just one).

Attributes
- Body: 3
- Quickness: 4
- Strength: 4
- Charisma: 5
- Intelligence: 5
- Willpower: 5
- Essence: 1.8
- Reaction: 3
- Magic: 3

Cyberware
- 300 Mp of memory
- Datajack
- Radio
- Smartgun Link

Dice Pools
- Astral (Defense)*: as Skill
- Astral (Dodge)*: 5
- Astral (Magic)*: 1
- Defense (Armed): 5
- Defense (Unarmed): 3
- Dodge: 3
- Magic: 1

Gear
- Ingram Smartgun [32 (clip), 5M3]
- Partial Heavy Armor (6/4)

Spells
- **Detection**
  - Analyze Device: 2
  - Clairvoyance: 1
  - Detect Enemies: 1

*Per **The Grimoire**

Skills
- Armed Combat: 5
- Etiquette (Corporate): 5
- Etiquette (Street): 6
- Firearms: 5
- Interrogation: 5
- Leadership: 6
- Negotiation: 5
- Sorcery: 1
- Unarmed Combat: 3

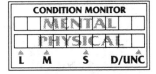

CONDITION MONITOR		
MENTAL		
PHYSICAL		
L	M	S	D/UNC

AGENT DELLA COOPER

Agent Cooper is much closer to the archetype of a Federal agent than is Drummond. She is in her early 30s, hard as steel, and sharp as a knife. Like Drummond, she is incorruptible, but she is much more likely to use the "hard option" in any confrontation (her rationale is that she would not have been called in if the situation was at all ambiguous).

Cooper has a deep hatred of the Humanis Policlub. When she was younger, Cooper fell deeply in love with an elf named Derek Rosebower. Unfortunately, Rosebower was in the wrong place at the wrong time and died in a drive-by shooting committed by a Humanis Policlub member. The policlub disclaimed responsibility, attributing the kill—rightly, as it turns out—to a deranged individual who only happened to be a Humanis member. Cooper rejected this explanation, of course, and blames the policlub for her lover's death. This event motivated Cooper to enter the Bureau.

Cooper would prefer to shoot Humanis Policlub members first and forget about the questions entirely. Drummond is able to keep her enthusiasm in check. If she is operating alone—or if, god forbid, Drummond is incapacitated or killed—she will geek Humanis members at every opportunity.

Attributes
Body: 5
Quickness: 3
Strength: 4
Charisma: 2
Intelligence: 4
Willpower: 4
Essence: 1.1
Reaction: 4
Magic: 2

Skills
Armed Combat: 6
Etiquette (Corporate): 4
Etiquette (Street): 4
Firearms: 5
Interrogation: 3
Leadership: 5
Negotiation: 2
Sorcery: 2
Unarmed Combat: 4

Cyberware
300 Mp of memory
Datajack
Low-Light Cybereyes w/flare compensation
Radio
Retractable Razors
Smartgun Link

Dice Pools
Astral (Defense)*: as Skill
Astral (Dodge)*: 4
Astral (Magic)*: 2
Defense (Armed): 6
Defense (Unarmed): 4
Dodge: 4
Magic: 2

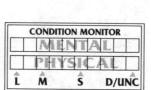

CONDITION MONITOR
MENTAL
PHYSICAL
L M S D/UNC

Gear
1 Offensive Grenade (6M3)
2 Concussion Grenades (4M3 Stun)
Ares Predator with Smartgun Link [10 (clip), 4M2]
FN HAR [20 (clip), 5M3]
Full Heavy Armor (8/6)

Spells
Detection
Detect Enemies: 1
Combat
Power Bolt: 1
Illusion
Invisibility: 2
*Per **The Grimoire**

RAM

In his early 30s, Ram is a nasty piece of work. As a kid, he honed his considerable computer skills by running the Pueblo Corporate Council Net naked.

Encounters with various forms of unpleasant black IC left him with brain damage. His intellect and abilities are undamaged, but his personality has warped. Ram is a classic sociopath: he believes that other people are merely tools to use and discard or obstacles to eliminate as quickly and brutally as possible. (He and Jesse make a great pair…) He works out of Denver as a decker-for-hire and maintains a first-class reputation. Unlike some deckers, Ram is almost as formidable outside the Matrix as in it.

Attributes
Body: 2
Quickness: 3
Strength: 2
Charisma: 1
Intelligence: 5
Willpower: 3
Essence: 1.8
Reaction: 4

CONDITION MONITOR
MENTAL
PHYSICAL
L   M   S   D/UNC

Cyberware
Datajack with 300 Mp memory

Dice Pools
Defense (Armed): 3
Defense (Unarmed): 2
Dodge: 3
Hacking: 11

Gear
3 Shuriken
Fairlight Excalibur with Level 2 Response Increase
Uzi III [16 (clip), 4M3]

Skills
Armed Combat: 3
Computer: 6
Computer (B/R): 3
Computer Theory: 4
Electronics: 4
Etiquette (Street): 2
Firearms: 3
Projectile Weapons: 2
Unarmed Combat: 2

Programs
Attack: 6
Bod: 6
Evasion: 6
Masking: 6
Medic: 2
Mirrors: 5
Sensors: 6
Shield: 4
Smoke: 5

In addition, Ram has a utility that gives him free access to SAN 0010AF in the Pueblo Net (see **Into the Fire**, p. 32). This utility is 8 Mp in size. Unlike the utility that the runners use, Ram's version does not contain the code that identifies it as being of Sioux manufacture (see **Into the Fire**).

He also has a program "key" that causes the Net's adaptive architecture to change. Specifically, this key causes the dataline that normally links SPU 5 to CPU 1 to shift so that it links SPU 5 to SPU 6. (This is described in detail in **Into the Fire**.) The key is a simple 1 Mp program.

JESSE JOHN

Jesse John was raised in the traditions of the Tsimshian tribe. He turned away from his heritage, however, and has long plotted the destruction of the Native American Nations. Jesse was slightly unbalanced even as a child, and over the years this imbalance has flowered into full-fledged madness. He accepted enough of his heritage that he was able to take advantage of the power available to him as a shaman. He originally used the Rat totem, but quickly perverted its precepts until he became a full-fledged Toxic shaman (see **The Grimoire**). Jesse combines a genius-level intelligence and an evil nature. Every action is focused toward his ultimate goal—destroying the NAN as a political force—and he will kill or destroy without a second thought anyone or anything that gets in his way.

Attributes

Body: 3
Quickness: 5
Strength: 2
Charisma: 1
Intelligence: 5
Willpower: 5
Essence: 6
Magic: 6
Reaction: 5

Cyberware

None

Dice Pools

Astral (Defense)*: as Skill
Astral (Dodge)*: 6
Astral (Magic)*: 6
Defense (Armed): 4
Defense (Unarmed): 3
Dodge: 5
Magic: 6

*Per **The Grimoire**

Skills

Armed Combat: 4
Conjuring: 6
Enchantment: 5
Etiquette (Street): 4
Etiquette (Tribal): 3
Firearms: 2
Magical Theory: 4
Sorcery: 6
Stealth: 4
Unarmed Combat: 3

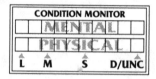

CONDITION MONITOR

MENTAL

PHYSICAL

L   M   S   D/UNC

Gear

Colt America L36 [9 (clip), 3M2]
Medicine Lodge Materials (2)
Medkit
Knife with Orichalcum (Rating 3)
Stimulant Patch (2)

Spells

Combat

Death Touch: 3
Fire Bolt: 5
Fireblast: 4
Mana Bolt: 4
Manablast: 3
Power Missile: 4
Stunblast: 2
Urban Renewal: 2

Detection

Clairvoyance (extended): 5

Illusion

Chaotic World: 2
Overstimulation: 5

Manipulation

Clout: 3
Levitate Item: 2
Turn to Goo: 4

Threat Rating: 6*

*Jesse's Threat Rating at the beginning of the adventure is 6. He gains an additional +1 bonus to his Threat Rating for each goal he reaches in the adventure (each time the runners fail to thwart his plans). The individual adventure sections indicate when each bonus should be added. Threat Ratings are discussed in detail in **The Grimoire**.

PLAYER HANDOUTS

TODAY'S HEADLINES:

INTERNATIONAL
•The San Francisco bay area was rocked by an earthquake measuring 5.5 on the Richter scale. California Free State officials said damage was not serious. San Francisco authorities were not commenting further.

LOCAL
•Thieves made off with nine Laubenstein paintings from the Laubenstein Plaza Hotel lobby gallery sometime late last week. The disappearance was discovered early Sunday, but hotel management waited to announce the loss, hoping to solve the matter internally.

BUSINESS
• Eurocar stocks soared in the wake of rumors that they will soon produce a high-powered, lower-priced car similar to the Westwind.
• Corporate mages are seeking a new image. A new professional organization hopes to set guidelines for appropriate behavior.

ENTERTAINMENT
• The Seattle Shakespeare Festival announced preliminary plans for next summer's Shakespeare in the Dome. They hope to stage *Macbeth*, *Coriolanus*, and *The Tempest* in the Kingdome next summer. The productions will feature large-scale battle scenes and spectacular live magic effects.

SPORTS
• Urban Brawl season opens in a week, and defending champions Sprawl Scummers say they're ready for all challengers.
• Mariners Manager Sludge Whittaker expressed outrage at the possibility of Shakespeare in the Dome next summer. "I don't trust that magic stuff. There could be some bad spirits hanging around when we play at home," Sludge said.

BODIES FOUND IN CEMETERY
M. Perneta

Residents near the Brando Memorial Cemetery were awakened last night by a series of explosions that rocked the neighborhood. Morning light revealed a number of bodies identified at press time as a vampire, a dzoo-noo-qua, four banshees, and an undetermined number of ghouls along with the dismembered bodies of members of the Church of the Whole Earth Inc. A nearby crypt had been opened, possibly forced by magic, though the body was not removed. Evidence of a fight was found within the structure.

The principle weapon of destruction, according to police, seemed to be explosive grenades of some kind. They are continuing to investigate.

NAN BREAKUP IMMINENT?
N. Findley

Political analysts are watching with great attention—and not a little trepidation—as tension among the members of the Native American Nations grows. "We have never seen negative dynamics at such a high level," Jeanine Hormsley, Fellow of the Annacis Institute, stated today. "Several sociometric indicators are already off the charts and the second derivative is increasing alarmingly." Alexis Potter, of the University of Washington International Relations Department, concurs. "Though the math certainly is indicative, you don't have to be a sociometricist to understand what's happening," she says. "The Sovereign Tribal Council is engulfed in petty bickering and the odds are that it will increase. Unless someone can engineer a device to calm those people down, I expect to see a breakup of the NAN within three months." For an analysis of the consequences for Seattle, see "Breakup—Boon or Disaster?"

DOWNTOWN POLICE SLAYING
L. Erickson

Late last night, an unidentified gunman entered the Seattle Downtown Lone Star precinct and opened fire with an assault rifle, killing two and injuring another. Officer Lucas Kidd was killed while attempting to protect Ken Shaker, the second fatality, from the gunman. Shaker had been deposited, unconscious, on the steps of the Lone Star building only a few hours before the shooting. It is not known if any witnesses saw him arrive. This source has learned that Shaker, a collant technician for the Renraku Corporation, was reported missing from the Arcology late last November. No further information was available.

The shooting and Shaker's whereabouts during the months he was missing are being investigated by the authorities.

BLAST RIPS BROTHERHOOD
D. Fister

Five were killed early this morning when a bomb exploded at the Universal Brotherhood Chapterhouse in Tacoma, Seattle.

Lone Star Commander Sam McMillin stated, "This terrorism against the Brotherhood must end. The Brotherhood is a fine, upstanding group that makes significant social contributions to our community and we will not tolerate actions such as these to be perpetrated against them!" A black Westwind 2000 was seen outside the Chapterhouse just before the blast.

The Brotherhood could not be reached for comment by press time.

TODAY'S HEADLINES:

INTERNATIONAL
•The San Francisco bay area was rocked by an earthquake measuring 5.5 on the Richter scale. California Free State officials said damage was not serious. San Francisco authorities were not commenting further.

LOCAL
•Thieves made off with nine Laubenstein paintings from the Laubenstein Plaza Hotel lobby gallery sometime late last week. The disappearance was discovered early Sunday, but hotel management waited to announce the loss, hoping to solve the matter internally.

BUSINESS
• Eurocar stocks soared in the wake of rumors that they will soon produce a high-powered, lower-priced car similar to the Westwind.
• Corporate mages are seeking a new image. A new professional organization hopes to set guidelines for appropriate behavior.

ENTERTAINMENT
• The Seattle Shakespeare Festival announced preliminary plans for next summer's Shakespeare in the Dome. They hope to stage *Macbeth*, *Coriolanus*, and *The Tempest* in the Kingdome next summer. The productions will feature large-scale battle scenes and spectacular live magic effects.

SPORTS
• Urban Brawl season opens in a week, and defending champions Sprawl Scummers say they're ready for all challengers.
• Mariners Manager Sludge Whittaker expressed outrage at the possibility of Shakespeare in the Dome next summer. "I don't trust that magic stuff. There could be some bad spirits hanging around when we play at home," Sludge said.

BODIES FOUND IN CEMETERY
M. Perneta
Residents near the Brando Memorial Cemetery were awakened last night by a series of explosions that rocked the neighborhood. Morning light revealed a number of bodies identified at press time as a vampire, a dzoo-noo-qua, four banshees, and an undetermined number of ghouls along with the dismembered bodies of members of the Church of the Whole Earth Inc. A nearby crypt had been opened, possibly forced by magic, though the body was not removed. Evidence of a fight was found within the structure.

The principle weapon of destruction, according to police, seemed to be explosive grenades of some kind. They are continuing to investigate.

FALSE ALARM AT GRAND COUNCIL LODGE
N. Findley

A special meeting of the Salish-Shidhe Council was disrupted yesterday when a faulty sensor in an air conditioning control room triggered a fire alarm. The Council Island Emergency Response Team was on the scene in moments and quickly determined that the alert was false. "The sensor was triggered when a bearing on a heat pump seized," explained an ERT spokesperson. "The bearing tore itself apart quite violently. It must have sounded like gunshots to anyone in the area." After the excitement of the alarm ended, the Council meeting continued peacefully. An accord was reached on several key issues. See "Political Watch" for an analysis of the meeting. Next week, the Council will send three representatives to a NAN Sovereign Tribal Council meeting. "This marks the beginning of an era of closer cooperation between NAN members," said Harold Gray Bear.

DOWNTOWN POLICE SLAYING
L. Erickson

Late last night, an unidentified gunman entered the Seattle Downtown Lone Star precinct and opened fire with an assault rifle, killing two and injuring another. Officer Lucas Kidd was killed while attempting to protect Ken Shaker, the second fatality, from the gunman. Shaker had been deposited, unconscious, on the steps of the Lone Star building only a few hours before the shooting. It is not known if any witnesses saw him arrive. This source has learned that Shaker, a collant technician for the Renraku Corporation, was reported missing from the Arcology late last November. No further information was available.

The shooting and Shaker's whereabouts during the months he was missing are being investigated by the authorities.

BLAST RIPS BROTHERHOOD
D. Fister

Five were killed early this morning when a bomb exploded at the Universal Brotherhood Chapterhouse in Tacoma, Seattle.

Lone Star Commander Sam McMillin stated, "This terrorism against the Brotherhood must end. The Brotherhood is a fine, upstanding group that makes significant social contributions to our community and we will not tolerate actions such as these to be perpetrated against them!" A black Westwind 2000 was seen outside the Chapterhouse just before the blast.

The Brotherhood could not be reached for comment by press time.

DANCNCHEKKERS PRIMER ON THE NATIVE AMERICAN NATIONS VOLUME ONE

NATIVE AMERICAN NATIONS

Welcome to the on-line version of *Danchekker's Primer on the Native American Nations, Volume 1*. This volume serves as a guide to understanding the traditions, economy, laws, people, and other aspects of the Pueblo Corporate Council, the Salish-Shidhe Council, the Sioux nation, and the Ute nation.

As with all the volumes in the *Danchekker's Primer* series, this book supplements and expands on the tribal-lands information included in most senior-high and university-preparation level courses. This information will be of value to students of sociology, anthropology, history, international relations, and government studies. Once again, it must be stressed that the *Danchekker's Primer* series is a supplement to—not a substitute for—standard classroom instruction and database research. Though this *Primer* contains much information drawn from the standard reference works on the subject, the student should read those reference works for him or herself.

The reader will note that this volume gives some prominence to events occurring in the 19th century and earlier. The reason is that, as a culture, Amerindians are bound more closely to their history than any other group in the world. Amerindians weave their past into the fabric of their present cultural traditions.

Every effort has been made to ensure the accuracy of this material, but the Native American Nations are dynamic, constantly changing entities. Danchekker's Primer Series Inc. accepts no responsibility for damage or loss resulting from information contained herein.

>>>>>[As with all of the Danchekker's Primer series, it's my considered advice that you trust the information contained herein about as far as you can spit a rat.

Good old Dr. Danchekker, friend to millions of lazy students. Why read the original reference works, why attend classes, when you can absorb it all in comfortably pre-digested form from the "lips" of kindly Dr. Danchekker?

If you can access this, welcome to the shadow edition of *Danchekker's Primer*. I love this guy Danchekker, you know? Or I would if he really existed. "Danchekker" is actually five researchers and three copywriters, all rolling in nuyen thanks to the success of that kindly persona, Dr. David Danchekker.

And that revelation, oh my friends, is an example of the deep background you can expect from this, the shadow edition. I and my associates will endeavor—as "Dr. Danchekker" might put it— to elucidate the more erroneous statements in the standard edition. If you've got the computing wherewithal, feel free to update our comments, because—as we have been informed— "the Native American Nations are dynamic entities." On the other hand, we take no responsibility for the accuracy of any of these third-party comments, either. Believe at your own risk...but you in the shadows know all about that.

Go to it, and leave no stone unturned. You'll be surprised at the creepy-crawlies you're going to find.]<<<<<
—Captain Chaos, Northwest Neo-Anarchists League (23:38:15/8-3-51)

>>>>>[I just heard that the long-awaited (yeah, right) Volume 2 is due soon on the net. Check it out, chummers. You'll love it just as much as Volume 1.]<<<<<
—Captain Chaos (17:32:25/8-10-51)

GENERAL HISTORY

The Native American Nations did not exist prior to the signing of the Treaty of Denver in 2018, but the events that made the founding of NAN inevitable had begun some 50 years earlier. During the 1980s and 1990s, tribal groups across North America began filing land claims against the governments then in power. These claims demanded that the tribal lands usurped when the "white man" (Anglos) spread westward across the continent be returned, or else that financial restitution be made. In most cases, the governments deeded back to the natives at least a portion of the lands that once were theirs, unable to pay the compensation the tribes demanded.

This trend was reversed during the first years of the 21st century. Under pressure from the megacorporations, which had gained true extraterritoriality with the Shiawase Decision of 2001, both the United States and Canadian governments began invoking the right of eminent domain and repossessing the lands granted to the native tribes only a decade or so before. Megacorporations and coalitions of (relatively) small companies such as National Oil were granted licenses to exploit the repossessed lands for their oil and mineral resources.

Needless to say, the native Americans to whom these lands belonged did not take kindly to this land grab, dubbed by the media "The Resource Rush." Angry and frustrated, the more radical elements founded the Sovereign American Indian Movement (SAIM). SAIM made their point by blockading important highways, a tactic also used by Canadian Amerindians in the early 1990s. The first blockade was negotiated to a peaceful settlement. When the tribes protested a second time with blockades, the Canadian and U.S. governments, backed by the security forces of various corporations, simply took them out in the most efficient manner possible. The casualties were surprisingly low (except in the confrontation discussed in the Sioux nation file), but the swift paramilitary response sent the leaders of SAIM an important message: the conflict had escalated.

The flashpoint came in 2009, when United Oil Industries announced that it had acquired the right to exploit the petrochemical resources in one-quarter of the remaining federal parks and one-tenth of the Indian lands, which the government had just confiscated. SAIM reacted immediately and decisively. A small band of commando-trained Amerindians—some of them one-time members of the USMC "Scalpel" Special Forces team—penetrated the Shiloh Launch Facility in northwest Montana, capturing the silo and gaining launch control of the 16-warhead "Lone Eagle" MIRV missiles within.

Issuing a demand for the return of all Indian land, the Shiloh raiders threatened to launch the silo's missiles. After ten days of tense negotiations, a U.S. Armed Forces "Delta" Crisis Response Team entered the silo complex. The penetration team "neutralized" the occupying force, but not before a single Lone Eagle missile was launched toward the Soviet Union.

Though the missile's warheads never detonated, there was still considerable fallout from the incident. When the North American public learned of the Lone Eagle crisis, the outcry was enormous. Goaded by corporate propagandists, the people began to blame SAIM, and by implication, all Native Americans. Lobby groups for the major corporations used the public outcry as "grass- roots support" for their pro- posals and pres- sured the U.S. government into passing the Re-Education and Relocation Act. (The Nepean Act, legitimizing similar camps, was signed into law in Canada on the same day.) These Acts called for anyone connected in any way to SAIM to be confined in so-called "re-education camps." Violent public hatred of Native Americans sent many thousands of Amerindians who had no connection with SAIM to the camps "for their own protection."

In a government economy measure, Congress and the Canadian Parliament contracted out management of the re-education camps to the corporations. Once the media spotlight was off the camps, conditions deteriorated drastically. Overcrowding, poor

sanitation, and insufficient medical care became the standard. The camps were virtual gulags, cut off from the rest of North American society. (Ironically, it was this very isolation that saved the Amerindians when VITAS swept the world in 2010.)

The next major act in the Amerindian drama took place on December 24, 2011. Daniel Howling Coyote, formerly Daniel Coleman and later Prophet of the Great Ghost Dance, led his followers out of the Abilene Re-Education Center. The guards opened fire on the natives as they walked to freedom, but no casualties were reported.

After Daniel Howling Coyote led his cadre of believers out from the Abilene REC compound, he dropped from public view for several years. Knowledge of his activities during that period is minimal, but it later became obvious that he was spreading word of his power. Native Americans, both those who were free and those incarcerated in camps or restricted to the ever-shrinking reservations, heard of a new prophet, a great shaman to whom the spirits had taught a powerful dance. These tales inspired others to escape from the camps and to wage a guerrilla war against their enemies—the U.S. and Canadian governments and the corporations. As their ancestors had a century and more ago, the Native Americans struck fast and hard, then faded back into the wilderness. Unlike their ancestors, they had access to the same technology as their enemy. They also wielded the powers of magic, powers that the Anglos had yet to admit existed.

In 2014, Daniel Coleman, now calling himself Howling Coyote, stepped out of the shadows. Backed by an elite core of fanatics, he announced the formation of the Native American Nations, a coalition of tribes. The NAN laid claim to all of North America, and demanded the immediate withdrawal of all persons of European, African, and Asian ancestry. NAN threatened magical retribution if their demand was not met.

The NAN's demands were ridiculed by the media and ignored by the government. Then Redondo Peak erupted, burying Los Alamos, New Mexico under a cloud of ash. Howling Coyote appeared in a vid-cast from a nearby Zuñi reservation, claiming credit for the disaster. The U.S. government reacted quickly, attempting to capture the self-proclaimed shaman by sending the Sixth Air Cavalry Battalion from Fort Hood, Texas. The assault team never reached its destination. Violent storms tore their aircraft from the sky, and by the time a second force was mobilized, Howling Coyote was long gone.

The guerrilla war escalated. The armed forces and corporate armies of Canada, the U.S., and Mexico failed to stop the raiders.

The U.S. passed the Resolution Act of 2016 to resolve "the Indian question" once and for all. The plan was total extermination of all Native American tribes. (No corresponding legislation was ever passed in either Canada or Mexico. Both governments simply gave corporate forces tacit approval to take whatever actions they saw fit. The two countries could thus claim that they had never legislated for genocide—though the results would certainly be the same.)

While the government and corporate forces planned their strategies for elimination, the followers of Daniel Howling Coyote planned their own strategy of resolution. The Great Ghost Dance began in 2017, as men and women of the tribes all across the continent performed the ritual Howling Coyote had taught them. They sang his songs and chanted his chants. Their power grew.

Freak weather and other uncanny disturbances disrupted troop and equipment movement, pushing back "H-hour" for what is now known as "The Genocide Campaign." Finally, however, the government and corporations across North America were ready to mobilize their forces. At 10:30 A.M. PST, August 17, 2017, the operation began to roll.

At 10:32 A.M. PST, Mount Hood, Mount Rainier, Mount St. Helens, and Mount Adams all erupted in cataclysmic fury. The Genocide Campaign ground to a halt. The Amerindians had made good on their threats, and no one could doubt their power again.

At the same time, Native American tribesmen and non-Indian sympathizers had occupied military bases in all three North American countries, demanding a multinational conference. Chastened and wary, the three governments sent representatives to Denver to negotiate with the Ghost Dancers. In 2018, the results of the negotiations were formalized in the Treaty of Denver.

In the treaty, the federal governments of the United States, Canada, and Mexico acknowledged the sovereignty of the Native American Nations (NAN) over most of western North America. The document outlined a ten-year population adjustment plan that would relocate all non-Indians off lands belonging to NAN. Provisions included the establishment of reservations for non-tribal peoples and corporations, the maintenance of Seattle as an extraterritorial extension of the United States, and the division of Denver between various signatories to the Treaty.

The Treaty of Denver failed to satisfy any of the parties involved, but the signatories could not agree on another alternative. The Treaty still stands as one of the best examples of compromise in the history of political conflict.

Legitimized at last, NAN named Daniel Howling Coyote as head of the Sovereign Tribal Council, NAN's governing body. Though he found it difficult to mediate among the bickering that now began between various factions, Howling Coyote was probably the only man who could still rally the loyalty of all sides. Without an external enemy to unite the tribes, the internecine squabbles grew more intense, particularly over the issue of the Awakened—the orks, dwarfs, trolls, and, most particularly, the elves—whom the tribal nations generally welcomed with open arms. In 2035, a major schism opened between the Tsimshian nation and the other members of NAN. Two years later, the elves of the Northwest announced the birth of Tir Tairngire (the land of promise) and seceded from NAN. Emboldened by the elves' move, Tsimshian also officially seceded in 2037. This second blow to the unanimity of the STC intensified the internal strife. Unable to maintain the solidarity of the organization he had brought into existence, Daniel Howling Coyote, Prophet of the Great Ghost Dance, resigned and withdrew from society.

Since then, internal dissention has settled down to a form of background noise. The members of the STC recognize the Council's importance—as a rallying point for the different nations and a vehicle to coordinate action, should another outside threat to NAN ever materialize. The individual nations each have their own form of government, social structure, and social mores. The STC has not been granted the power to meddle in tribal affairs, and probably never will be.

- NELSON -

SALISH-SHIDHE COUNCIL

FACTS AT A GLANCE

Population: 10,118,000

Human:	63%
Elf:	13%
Dwarf:	12%
Ork:	9%
Troll:	2%
Other:	1%

Per Capita Income: 18,500¥
Below Poverty Level: 31%
On Fortune's Active Traders List: 0%
Corporate Affiliation: 10%
Education:
High School Equivalency: 53%
College Equivalency: 24%
Advanced Studies Certificates: 9%
Regional Telecom Grid Access: NA/NAN/SSC
Note: These statistics do not include Seattle.

CLIMATE

The Salish-Shidhe Council includes most of what was once the state of Washington and southern British Columbia. Summertime temperatures hover around the low 20s, occasionally peaking at 30 degrees Celsius, though this is rare. In the winter, the temperature stays at approximately freezing. Snow is rare on the coast, but it has closed passes through the Cascade range, sometimes for several days at a time. This area has a heavy annual rainfall with normal cloud cover of 50 percent in all seasons but the summer.

>>>>>[They used to call this area the "Evergreen Playground." More cynical, rain-hating types dubbed it the "Ever-gray Pee-ground."]<<<<<
—Tab (11:21:49/3-21-52)

>>>>>[I know some people think it's gray and depressing here for much of the year, but I like a place with real seasons. We also don't have to worry about the bad storms that trash the east and Gulf coasts.]<<<<<
—Woppler the Weatherman (19:28:47/3-28-52)

Along the coast of the Olympic Peninsula, morning and evening fogs are common. Major storms are rare, though some areas achieve an average wind speed as high as 25kph.

ACCESS

Plane

In addition to Seattle, three other major international airports serve the Salish-Shidhe Council: Vancouver, Bellingham, and Spokane. Vancouver International Airport's runways are long enough to accommodate the largest of the suborbital and semiballistic carriers. Spokane and Bellingham can only handle medium-range 797-class and V/STOL traffic.

>>>>>[Vancouver can take the big planes, but just barely. Landing in one of the big ones is always a good way to pump up your heart, particularly when approaching from the east. The west end of the main east-west runway is extended out from the shore on a causeway. When you run out of runway, you go for a sail. And your typical suborbital floats slightly worse than a brick. Some heavily loaded planes cut it so close that when they roll to a stop, their nose is hanging out over the Pacific.]<<<<<
—Davey (23:30:04/6-18-52)

Three major short-haul carriers connect the major Salish-Shidhe airports with the other cities of the nation: Cascade Air, Air West, and Salish Transport. A number of "sky cab" services run on an on-call, rather than scheduled, basis.

>>>>>[Stay away from Air West, chummers. People in the know call it "Scare West," and with good reason. Last year three planes made, shall we say, inadequate landings in the inner harbor at Victoria. Spu-LASH.]<<<<<
—Sky Pilot (08:36:40/5-24-52)

Automobile or Bus

The main land routes into the Salish-Shidhe Council are I-5 north from Portland (Tir Tairngire), Route 97 south from Hazelton (Tsimshian), Route 84 to 82 northeast from Salt Lake City, and Route 90 east from Butte. Whippet Bus Lines and Golden Eagle Transit run regularly along the main routes and between major population centers.

>>>>>[The bus service is very good, even on the routes into Seattle that go through the Barrens. Of course, the buses on that route are a tad slow from the weight of the armor.]<<<<<
—Lily (16:59:28/7-19-52)

Sea

During the summer months, the Salish-Shidhe Council runs a ferry service up the coast from Port Hardy on northern Vancouver Island to Prince Rupert in Tsimshian lands. This ferry route, which follows the scenic Inside Passage, is served by standard-hull ships rather than the fast multi-hull or hydroplane vessels used elsewhere in North America. This means the journey takes about twelve hours. The ferry trip is intended as a tourist excursion more than anything else, though some business travelers occasionally use it.

Black Ball Ferry, the same company that provides three-way service between Vancouver, Victoria, and Seattle, offers scenic cruises down the coast to San Francisco. These cruises are mainly for tourists already in the Salish-Shidhe nation, but there is a provision for one-way passengers to board the vessel in San Francisco. Such passengers must show valid Salish-Shidhe visas and travel permits, however.

>>>>>[Or you can bribe the purser. This is usually an easy process, but it might get difficult to prove once you're at sea. Your "purchased" purser might decide, for his own peace of mind, that it would be better all around if he took your bribe, stashed you aboard, then reported the "armed and dangerous stowaway" to the captain and the ship's security guards once your ship is safely launched. If the guards geek you, you'll be in no position to tell anyone that you greased the purser's palm. What a deal, huh?]<<<<<
—Zeebee (08:39:08/1-16-52)

TRIBAL DEMOGRAPHICS

The major tribes in the Salish-Shidhe nation are the Salish, Sinsearach, Makah, Cascade Crow, Cascade Ork, and Nootka. Every resident of the Salish-Shidhe nation is aligned with a tribe. The approximate numerical breakdown follows.

Salish	25%
Makah	16%
Cascade Crow	14%
Sinsearach	11%
Nootka	10%
Cascade Ork	9%
Other	15%

The other category is made up of many smaller tribal groups. These groups range from semi-organized bands like the Musqueam and the Squamish, each numbering several hundred, down to tiny bands of 20 or so members, such as the elven Séluné.

The great majority of the population is Amerindian. Only 5 percent of the total population comprises true "pinkskins." (In this context, the word refers to non-Amerinds who have fully adopted the native way of life and are affiliated with certain tribes.) Most of the pinkskins have joined the Nootka tribe, which is located around the port of Vancouver and further north. A number have joined the Salish, and a few the Makah. Several semi-tribal bands of pinkskins also live in Salish-Shidhe lands. The most widely known is the small but vociferous Tsawassen band, who tried to block the development of the Vancouver International Airport in 2047 as a protest against "intrusive technology."

>>>>>[It's interesting to note that, in general, the pinkskins are more vehemently back-to-the-land than any native tribal group. Though you can't help but admire their dedication to their goal, it seems to me that they represent the fanaticism of the newly converted.]<<<<<
—Holly (16:36:01/5-5-52)

>>>>>[A further clarification, since there've been some questions. "Pinkskin" is most commonly used to refer to those of completely non-Amerindian descent. NAN, in its early days, knew it was going to need a massive population influx because they were throwing the majority, whiteskins, out of the territory. They decided that if you could adequately prove even the slightest trace of Amerindian blood, you would be treated as a full blood. Pinkskin now refers to those who live in NAN lands, but have no Amerindian blood.]<<<<<
—The The (12:41:15/6-18-52)

Besides the pinkskins, very few other non-Amerindians live and work within the Salish-Shidhe nation. These few have almost always been recruited from elsewhere by an individual group for a specific purpose. For example, this category includes several of the watch supervisors at the Gaeatronics single-fusion plant in Olympia.

>>>>>[Okay, chummer, there are a few. Two, to be exact. And they're tokens. *And* they're watched closer than you'd believe possible.]<<<<<
—Teaser (12:30:32/8-1-52)

The nation usually registers an average of several hundred tourists at any given time.

Within the Salish-Shidhe nation, the individual tribes keep to themselves. Each has its own territory, its own way of life, and very nearly its own economy. Tribes will cooperate on a task that is obviously in the best interest of all parties, but surprisingly little intermixing takes place otherwise, except in Seattle and Vancouver.

As discussed in the **Government** section, each tribe governs itself to a greater or lesser degree, and all but the smallest has a representative on the Salish-Shidhe Council. This system prevents one tribal group from usurping political power from another or otherwise gaining an unfair advantage. Relations are good between the tribes.

>>>>>[With the possible exception of the Cascade Trogs, er, Cascade Orks. Nobody likes them much.]<<<<<
—Vic (19:33:41/8-23-52)

>>>>>[And vice versa, breeder.]<<<<<
—Cascade Trog (09:06:02/8-25-52)

>>>>>[All racial animosity aside, there *is* some trouble on the Salish-Shidhe Council concerning the Cascade Ork tribe. Evidence indicates that the tribe is engaged in illegal activities, including some that might cause political backlash against the entire Salish-Shidhe nation. Even though this same evidence implicates the Cascade Ork Council (albeit circumstantially), the tribal council refuses to consider it a serious problem. They accept the orks' claim that the activities are the work of "malcontents and strangers."]<<<<<
—Holly (15:09:33/8-30-52)

>>>>>[What kind of thing could backlash on an entire nation?]<<<<<
—Devon (21:55:43/9-26-52)

>>>>>[Cascade Ork is involved in the illegal t-bird runs taking BTL chips and other controlled substances into Seattle and elsewhere (and don't try to deny it, boys). The UCAS government and the Seattle local government, among others, are putting pressure on the S-S Council to stop their people from aiding and abetting the riggers with rest, recreation, and refit. The S-S Council in turn puts pressure on the Cascade Ork Council, but the orks just say, "Wasn't us, guys." Seattle and UCAS are both getting a mite testy at this point.]<<<<<
—SPD (01:47:29/9-27-52)

HISTORY AND CULTURE

Historically, this region was home to a number of tribes that no longer play a large role on the stage of Amerindian affairs. Before the 21st century dawned, the dominant tribes were the Bella Coola, Chinook, Haida, Klikitat, Kwakiutl, Nootka, Quileute, Quinault, Tlingit, and Tsimshian. Of these, only the Nootka tribe is still a significant presence in Salish-Shidhe lands. The others have been absorbed by other tribes, moved north into Tsimshian lands, or simply ceased to exist. (The "evaporation" of tribes is discussed later in this section.) The tribes now dominant in the region were only minor players in the past.

The Amerindians of the Pacific Northwest were among the last tribes to come into contact with European settlers and explorers. It was not until almost 1800 that traders made an impact on the tribes' way of life. By the turn of the 19th century, fur trading with Europeans flourished among the coastal tribes, and iron tools purchased from Anglo traders were quickly adopted by native carvers.

Elsewhere in North America, the arrival of the Europeans began the end of the Amerindian way of life. Not so in the Pacific Northwest. The tribes in this region, instead of resisting change, assimilated the European way of life. Some fishermen bought motorboats and sold their catches to commercial packers. Other Amerindians took jobs in canneries, or grew and sold potatoes to the European settlers.

Canadian law regarding Amerindians eventually led to the decline of the major tribes. "Status Indians"—those who lived on registered reservations—received various benefits, including decreased taxation, the right to limited self-governance, even a guaranteed yearly income. These benefits were not available to Indians who moved off the reservation, even if they left to take a job in the "outside world." Many of the older tribe members appreciated being paid "just for being an Indian." But for the younger, more ambitious members of the tribes, this was not enough. They wanted to make their own way in the Anglos' world, and gave up their status to do so. Slowly but inevitably, this led to a "brain drain" of the tribes, a cultural evaporation that took place as the young and energetic turned away from the heritage prescribed for them by law. Many dominant tribes declined.

The Amerindians of the Northwest were generally more band-oriented than tribe-oriented. The bands belonged to tribes, but individual loyalties were focused on the band. During the land claims and environmental movements of the 1980s and 1990s, it was individual bands such as the Mount Curry and Musqueam that moved to the forefront of the struggle, attempting to wrest control of their lands from the government.

It was only in the latter half of the first decade of the 21st century that the individual bands began to cooperate and form full-fledged tribes. Perhaps surprisingly, the tribes that "reformed" were not those that had been pre-eminent a century and more before, but others such as the Salish, the Cascade, and the Makah. This was true in Salish-Shidhe territory; the story is somewhat different in Tsimshian. Certainly, bands that were part of the formerly dominant tribes were still in existence, though much smaller than they had been. For one reason or another, they had "missed the boat." By the time they recognized the direction in which events were heading, and began to operate in a coordinated manner, other tribes had already established their power in the region. Many historians claim that this miscalculation caused the near-disappearance of several historically large tribes: because they would have little say in the future of the region, the majority of members deserted the tribal way of life forever.

In 2021, goblinization added a new wrinkle to the strained social fabric of the region. Though local bands and tribes prided themselves on the strength of their brotherhood with their own members, this assertion proved to be largely talk when approximately 10 percent of the population metamorphosed into orks and trolls. Regardless of their positions in the tribes prior to goblinization, the newly Awakened were generally feared, even hated, by their once-sworn brothers.

Some of the Awakened remained in their tribal groups and tried to claim their rights and freedoms as members in good standing. They were rejected. All but a very few were forced to withdraw from their communities, and struggled to make a life for themselves away from all they held dear. Slowly, inevitably, these Awakened banded together with others of their kind.

>>>>>[Your story is true, but it doesn't capture the full reality of the situation. The new tribes are made up of people from different bands, different tribes, different traditions, even different cultures. All they have in common is a biological change—which, after all, is only a superficial factor. It's a significant factor, more so when you tie in the reactions of their peer groups. But even a powerful reason for doing so doesn't make creating a new society an easy thing to do. The people who set up the communities of the Awakened were very dedicated to what they were doing. Otherwise they'd never have made the mental effort to overcome their own prejudices. Frag, I don't know if that even makes sense...]<<<<<
     —Holly (18:15:52/3-16-52)

>>>>>[You've got it, Holly. Those were interesting times.]<<<<<
     —Sarah Bright Water (15:34:58/5-10-52)

The first new tribe to apply for membership in the Salish-Shidhe Council was the Sinsearach, an association of young elves originally from other tribal groups. In view of the widely held prejudices of the day, it was surprising that the Sinsearach also included a relatively large number of pinkskin elves—elves of non-Amerindian descent who saw the tribal way of life as an attractive alternative to a progressively harsher urban lifestyle. The Sinsearach were quickly followed by the Cascade Ork, an association of orks, trolls, and a few dwarfs. The initial Cascade Ork tribe drew heavily from the Awakened of the Cascade Crow; soon, however, orks and trolls from other tribes and a large contingent of pinkskin orks joined their number.

Initially, the Sinsearach tribe was considerably smaller than the dominant Salish. Elves from elsewhere along the Pacific coast began to flock to Salish-Shidhe territory (which, at the time, extended as far south as Redding, in what had been California), and the numbers of the Sinsearach grew at an alarming rate. The speed of this growth began to worry the other tribes in the region.

>>>>>[...and everybody in Seattle.]<<<<<
     —SPD (19:40:56/2-27-52)

The Salish majority tried to create immigration laws to stem the flood of mostly pinkskin elves into the nation. The Sinsearach representatives blocked this move—but were outvoted when the other Salish-Shidhe tribes unexpectedly threw their weight behind the Salish. The elves interpreted the move as a racially motivated action. They began to wonder how long it would be before the Council would begin to actively oppress the elves already within the borders, and if they would take such drastic measures to keep new elves from moving into the territory.

>>>>>[An argument totally lacking in logic.]<<<<<
     —Gillian Morningsong (12:59:45/6-10-52)

>>>>>[Racism, perceived racism, and the response to both are rarely possessed of any great logic, my lady.]<<<<<
     —Tal Gilgalad (10:06:41/7-1-52)

This was the issue that split the Sinsearach tribe. One faction believed, despite the actions of the other tribes, that it would be to their greatest benefit to stay within the Salish-Shidhe Council structure. The second faction, which was smaller, but much more vocal, believed their only future lay separate from the Council. The Sinsearach broke into two distinct tribes, split geographically as well as politically. The northern tribe retained the name Sinsearach, the southern tribe took the name Cénesté, Elvish for "The Forsaken." This group repudiated all ties and duty to the Salish-Shidhe Council and welcomed any elven immigrants who wished to join them. In 2035, the Cénesté declared themselves the sovereign nation of Tir Tairngire.

>>>>>[Danchekker makes it sound very easy. It wasn't. We made heart-wrenching choices, and we have to live with our decisions. The genesis of Tir Tairngire was as joyful and tragic an event as any in the history of mankind.]<<<<<
    —Tinuviel (15:13:18/1-30-52)

>>>>>[Ya know, sometime I'd like to find out just where all this "elvish" stuff comes from. Some of it's Celtic, but some of it ain't...]<<<<<
    —Mr. Biggs (05:52:12/2-12-52)

Very few residents of the Salish-Shidhe nation wear the traditional clothing of the past because it is simply not practical in the modern world. Some traditionalists wear conical hats woven from finely twisted spruce roots, but tribal members who adhere this closely to the past are rare. The vast majority of the nation's residents wear contemporary clothing, preferably natural fabrics. Any other indication of their heritage is usually limited to feathers or other fetishes worn in the hair, a hatband, or somewhere else on their person.

Traditional handicrafts, such as wood and stone carving, still find expression in the Salish-Shidhe nation. The Makah and the Nootka are the main repositories of these skills, and both tribes are world-renowned for the quality of the carvings they sell.

>>>>>[The sale of their artwork makes up a large part of the Nootka's economy.]<<<<<
    —The Keynesian Kid (21:01:28/6-6-52)

>>>>>[The Cascade Orks also sell a lot of "traditional native artwork," often at vastly inflated prices, that is accompanied by "certificates of authenticity." The "traditional artwork" is actually turned out by computer-controlled lathes and CNC machinery, and the "certificates of authenticity" are run off by the thousands on photocopiers.]<<<<<
    —Togo (06:24:48/4-30-52)

>>>>>[What's your point?]<<<<<
    —Collector (10:27:15/6-27-52)

A TRIBE IN PERSPECTIVE: THE NOOTKA

Nootka villages once dotted the coastline of northwestern Washington state and the west coast of Vancouver Island. The Nootka were known for the beauty and seaworthiness of their cedar canoes, which they used for hunting and fishing and for raids on other Amerindian tribes.

>>>>>[Some historians claim that the techniques of my people influenced the New England designers of the American clipper ships in the early 1800s. How the knowledge crossed the continent is an interesting question, however.]<<<<<
    —Dan George (13:46:44/8-10-52)

In general, the Nootka way of life was little different from that of the other tribes in the Northwest. The tribe was almost completely dependent on fishing for survival, though with the arrival of the Europeans, some members of the Nootka became heavily involved in the fur trade. The Nootka tribe was responsible for several interesting local customs, including the use of Dentalium shells as a kind of currency (this in contrast to the other tribes of the region, who subsisted entirely on a barter economy), an economic system eventually adopted by other groups. They were also unique in marketing wooden products to the outside world. Nootka craftsmen became famous for their remarkably detailed wood work, which included mechanical devices such as puppets and masks with movable parts.

The Nootka tribe suffered greatly from cultural evaporation. By the last quarter of the 20th century, the Nootka way of life had almost vanished. The language was still spoken, and some remembered the old beliefs and customs, but the tribe as a cultural force had essentially vanished.

This trend was reversed in the early years of this century, due mainly to the efforts of one man. Chief Harold Jim was the hereditary chief of the Nootka tribe. Unlike previous chiefs, however, Jim was only in his mid-20s when he accepted his position. He had spent several years away from the reservation taking a degree in Marketing and Business Management at the University of Washington. When he returned to lead his tribe, he brought back with him a burning desire to see his people take their rightful place on the world stage—and the skills necessary to bring it about. Now, for the first time, the Nootka's chief truly understood the modern world. He had a vision for how the tribe could meet modern culture on the tribe's terms.

Under Chief Jim, Nootka elders learned that the ancient ways need not be totally at odds with the contemporary world, while the young, who had been steadily moving away from the tribe, discovered that pride in their heritage did not have to be discarded in order to make their way outside the native community. The tribe grew as "lapsed" members returned. Chief Jim began to create an image for the tribe in the news and in the minds of the area's non-native residents. All his efforts led to what would become Jim's finest hour. He brought to court the first land claims against the British Columbia provincial government, on behalf of the Nootka tribe as a whole, rather than individual bands.

>>>>>[I knew Chief Jim at the time of the court case. He knew enough about the Anglos' system to turn it against them. He hired Anglo lawyers, the best that money could buy, and provided all the staff work they needed. The court case was a joke. The provincial government expected the Nootka lawyers to be a couple of natives with basic law degrees from no-name colleges. What they faced was a whole fragging battery of high-priced legal eagles from the best firms in Toronto and New York. Chief Jim even brought in a constitutional specialist from London, England, to analyze the old British North America Act on which a large part of the government's claim was based. It was a turkey shoot. In the first five minutes, it was obvious who'd win. The government filed for continuances and postponements, and tried to get the whole thing thrown out on a technicality...even challenged the credentials of the English fixer. (Bad move.) The whole thing was a blow out. Chief Jim was a hero, and rightly so. He didn't try to do it all himself, he hired the right people for the job. That's the mark of a great leader.]<<<<<
—David (12:14:25/2-10-52)

Chief Jim pressed his claim in the courts, departing from the usual blockade tactics favored by other Amerindian nations, and achieved an unmitigated success.

Under Chief Jim, the Nootka were the first Northwestern tribe to join the SAIM movement. Jim was named to the governing council, and served the movement well until his death in 2012.

>>>>>[His murder, you mean, chummer. Jim was assassinated, probably by members of the Alamos 20K group.]<<<<<
—Otter (17:12:25/3-19-52)

>>>>>[Never proven. Sure, his death was a freak accident—he got hit by a truck when its brakes failed—but coincidences do happen. The investigation showed that the brakes really did go by themselves. There was no evidence, and I repeat, no evidence of tampering.]<<<<<
—Skeleton Hunter (23:54:14/4-2-52)

Chief Jim's influence on the Nootka tribe was powerful when he was alive. If anything, it seemed to become even more profound after his death. Jim was honored as a martyr. The Nootka, who up to this point had been basically apolitical, gave the SAIM cause their full support. This support extended to NAN after its founding by Daniel Howling Coyote.

The Nootka tribe has a strong sense of pride and cultural heritage. It was their pride that prompted them to delay joining the Salish-Shidhe Council.

>>>>>[Of course we delayed. We *should* have established a separate Nootka nation.]<<<<<
—Otter (17:15:25/3-19-52)

>>>>>[Sorry, Otter, but you simply couldn't have gone it alone, and your tribal leadership eventually recognized that. (Unfortunately, it was a little late by then and you ended up getting boned for it. See my comments under Economy.)]<<<<<
—Holly (15:12:33/12-10-52)

The Nootka have drifted away from the principles espoused by Chief Jim. His strength lay in his willingness to borrow any influences from the modern world that would help to preserve what was valuable in the traditional Nootka lifestyle. He never turned his back on technology if that technology had value to his tribe. Today, the Nootka shun most forms of technology simply on principle, without evaluating them as potentially useful tools. Magic, which is common among the tribe, has made up for some of the loss, but the standard of living among the Nootka has declined since Chief Jim's day. Many traditionalists have begun to appear among the Nootka, wearing the woven cape and hat that was common two centuries ago. Wood carving has seen a renaissance, and several Nootka communities are almost completely dependent on the sale of their artwork for survival.

ECONOMY

Each of the constituent tribes and tribal groups of the Salish-Shidhe Council has its own economy, ranging from a fairly sophisticated pseudo-corporate system among the Salish and Makah to a rudimentary barter economy among the Tsawassen.

Some overlap exists between the individual "sub-economies," of course. All tribes use the same currency, the nuyen, and all pay a share of the upkeep costs for the facilities on Council Island. In addition, all tribes subsidize the Salish's expenses for maintaining the Ranger Forces and Coast and Border Patrols.

>>>>>[And a few of the tribes aren't too jazzed by that arrangement. The Cascade Orks don't like paying for the Rangers or the Border Patrol, because it's usually those forces who mess up the orks' more, er, innovative money-making schemes. And the Nootka aren't happy about it either. They'd be quite happy to just ignore Seattle and let it die from its own poisons. They consider the money spent on the Rangers, whose major job is to patrol the enclave border around Seattle, as completely wasted. But both groups know that they have to pay the tab if they want to be on the Council, because if they're not on the Council, they have no say in major policy decisions. As some philosopher once said, "Life is full of choices, but you never get to make any."]<<<<<
— Harpo (13:49:04/2-18-52)

>>>>>[That "philosopher" was Linus Van Pelt.]<<<<<
— Bung (11:56:30/2-19-52)

>>>>>[Who?]<<<<<
— Boris (16:00:45/2-22-52)

>>>>>[Skip it.]<<<<<
— Bung (15:36:31/3-1-52)

The level of technology in the Salish-Shidhe nation varies from tribe to tribe. The Salish are by far the most technologically inclined. This makes sense, because they own and manage Gaeatronics, the corporation providing Seattle and most of the Salish-Shidhe nation with power. Gaeatronics is a highly efficient, well-managed enterprise, using the optimum mix of three different power-generation techniques: solar, wind, and fusion. The Gaeatronics power grid is so effective that its output far exceeds demand, allowing the Salish-Shidhe Council to sell power to Tir Tairngire and the California Free State. In response to the serious concerns of the entire nation, all three technologies are clean.

>>>>>[Tracts of land are covered with solar cell arrays or with phalanxes of windmills. Cooling stacks pour smoke into the atmosphere at the fusion plant. And how does Gaeatronics plan to handle the nuclear waste? This is clean?]<<<<<
— Richard Sea Otter (06:39:37/11-3-52)

>>>>>[Okay, point by point. The tracts of land covered by solar arrays and windmills are in the arid interior, around Moses and Soap lakes, where nothing grows but horned toads and rattlesnakes. And they don't seem to mind the windmills. Cooling stacks don't release smoke, they release steam: pure, uncontaminated water vapor, just like a cloud. Fusion, at least, the single-fusion process used by Gaeatronics, produces no nuclear waste. The reaction product is helium, which the S-S Council sells to Cal Free. More fragging neo-Luddites!]<<<<<
— Technocrat (00:31:53/11-13-52)

>>>>>[The issue still remains of what we will do with the fusion plant in 15 or so years when continuous neutron bombardment has made the metal components of the core so brittle that the unit must be decommissioned. Do we just seal it in concrete and forget about it? For 17,000 years? I assure you, I'm no neo-Luddite; I merely have concerns and questions.]<<<<<
— Warden (23:57:49/11-28-52)

Next highest in technical sophistication are the Makah. Their main source of income is forestry, normally considered a relatively "low-tech" industry. The Makah have raised it to a fine art, however, with innovative harvesting techniques and highly sophisticated sylviculture programs. With selective logging and judicious replanting, sometimes with genetically manipulated strains of trees, the Makah are receiving better yields from their forests than they would with clear-cutting. This also allows them to maintain lush forestation and the appearance and ecosystems associated with old-growth forests.

>>>>>[A tree farm is not a forest.]<<<<<
— Western Wilderness Committee (19:42:54/2-4-52)

>>>>>[The Makah are doing it right at the processing end of it, too. Their sawmills are efficient—almost no wastage—and their pulp mills are squeaky-clean. They use a neat twist on high-temperature hydrogen bleaching, avoiding dioxins, and all their plants have huge heat sinks beneath them to minimize the thermal shock on the river when they release their cooling water. Efficiency is unbelievable.]<<<<<
— Hipp (11:15:35/6-15-52)

>>>>>[According to my map, the Makah hold a bunch of old USN facilities. What the frag are a bunch of ignorant savages doing with a Trident sub base?]<<<<<
— Tober (21:41:33/7-14-52)

>>>>>[You'll never know…till we want you to, Anglo.]<<<<<
— Koitla (11:29:21/7-22-52)

Of the major tribes, the Nootka have by far the least technology, and in fact show a strong aversion to technology in any form. They live much the same way their ancestors did, fishing, hunting, and practicing limited agriculture and animal husbandry. What little light industry is allowed in the Salish-Shidhe nation, however, is localized around Prince George—nominally within Nootka territory.

>>>>>[This was based on an early decision of the Council, before the Nootka tribe became a member. (When the Council was first formed, the Nootka wanted nothing to do with it, and decided to go their own way. When they discovered the existence of manufacturing plants in their territory, they realized that joining the Council might be a good idea. By then, however, it was too late. They were unable to get enough support from the Council to close down the plants.) I know that sounds bad, like the Council really stuck it to the Nootka. The fact of the matter is that the area was far from the main population concentration of the Nootka—in fact, far from any population center, since Prince George had become a ghost town. Since the industry moved in, Prince George is once again thriving, and lots of the less adamantly back-to-the-land Nootka have found work there.]<<<<<
—Holly (15:02:26/12-10-52)

>>>>>[Holly, my dear, I read your books and admired them greatly, but on this you're quite wrong. The Nootka got royally drek-fragged, in the modern argot. The land was ours, and the land was raped. And since we Nootka believe we are the land and the land is us...well, the logic is obvious.]<<<<<
—Chilko (21:22:41/12-24-52)

The other tribes fall somewhere between the two extremes. An interesting case is the Cascade Ork tribe. Of all the Salish-Shidhe tribes, they seem the least concerned about the land. The tribe operates several mines in the Cascades, and are notably lax about site reclamation and effluent control. Tailings from a mine in the Cle Elum area have contaminated a small river that flows southwest into the Sinsearach lands.

>>>>>[And are the dandelion-eaters ever hopping mad about that one.]<<<<<
—Vic (19:41:42/8-23-52)

>>>>>[Mighty nice mine you boys have got there. Be a real shame if it has an accident...]<<<<<
—Muncher (13:15:46/9-17-52)

Initially, the Cascade Ork mined only small amounts of nickel and tungsten. In 2036, a routine assay of an area near Peshastin turned up an astounding concentration of uranium. Though most developed nations use fusion as a source of power, several developing or regressing nations use fission, and require quantities of plutonium or uranium. Therefore the demand, and thus the price, for uranium is still considerable. The Cascade Ork had stumbled upon a potential jackpot, and did not waste a moment putting all their efforts into making it pay off.

The other members of the Council regularly call for and receive votes of censure against the Cascade Ork for their mining practices, however, the Council has no authority to take disciplinary action. Also, because of the original Council charter, they have no choice but to allow the Cascade Ork to transport their metals through Council lands to port.

The Salish-Shidhe nation imports and exports very little. Exports comprise forest products and some high-value-added manufactured goods. In addition, the nation exports the uranium mined in the Cascades. The majority of goods are shipped by sea, almost all through Vancouver. (Though this requires some land transportation, it avoids negotiation with the UCAS to use the Port of Seattle.) Bellingham is a distant second choice for shipping. Uranium shipments present quite a different case, however. The Council pressured the UCAS government into allowing them to use the Port of Seattle. This no doubt cost them certain concessions, but the Council decided the cost was worth the benefit of avoiding an accident in Vancouver or Bellingham harbor.

>>>>>[Yeah, just fragging typical, right? The fragging redskins don't want the nasty drek going through their nice, clean harbor, so they dump it onto Seattle. And our so-called government says "Yes, sir, no, sir, give it to me again, sir." Frag! I don't know who I hate more, the fragging Indians or the fragging politicians.]<<<<<
—Proud Anglo (21:59:44/10-24-52)

>>>>>[Yeah, well, abusive comments aside, it *doesn't* seem like a good deal for Seattle, and I think Governor Schultz should fight it.]<<<<<
—Lance (10:28:19/10-29-52)

>>>>>[Forget it. Schultz gets two paychecks, one from the Government Treasury and one from Council Island. Any bets on which one's bigger?]<<<<<
—Nova (13:15:47/11-9-52)

>>>>>[Long though the list of Schultz's perfidies may be, that isn't one of them. Sorry, Nova.]<<<<<
—Captain Chaos (14:02:43/11-9-52)

Imports are limited to certain foodstuffs and some technology.

The economic structure varies from tribe to tribe, and so does the standard of living. It is highest among the Salish and Makah, and lowest among the small barter-economy groups.

>>>>>[Depends on how you measure the standard of living, doesn't it? They don't have any nuyen, but they might have a better quality of life than you do, chummer.]<<<<<
—Nightwind (03:58:53/3-10-52)

>>>>>[I don't do subjective issues like quality of life, since I can't quantify it. But let's talk cost differentials. You'll notice that the majority of items I list are cheaper than in Seattle, including some of the tech-toys. The issue is availability. The prices I give are what you'll pay if you could find what you want, and there's no guarantee of that. I'll flag limited-access stuff. For those items, you might be better off going to the Cascade Ork and putting in an order to be delivered via the next t-bird run.

SALISH-SHIDHE COST OF LIVING

ITEM	COST
Weaponry	
Ammunition	95% (2)
Explosives	80% (4)
Firearm Accessories	110% (3)
Firearms	95% (1)
Melee Weapons	95%
Projectile Weapons	90%
Throwing Weapons	95%
Armor and Clothing	
Armor	120% (5)
Security and Surveillance	
Communications	95%
Security Devices	95%
Surveillance Countermeasures	110%
Surveillance Measures	95%
Survival Gear	70%
Vision Enhancers	100%
Lifestyle	
Lifestyle	120%
Electronics	
Electronics	95%
Cybertech	
Biotech	140%
Bodyware	130%
Cyberdecks	200%
Headware	130% (6)
Internals	130%
Programs	200%
Magical Equipment	
Hermetic Library	100%
Magical Supplies	80%
Magical Weapons	95%
Power Foci	80%
Ritual Sorcery Materials	100%
Spell Foci	80%
Vehicles	
Aircraft	130%
Boats	100%
Ground Vehicles	100%
Military Vehicles	300%+ (7)

Cost of Living—Notes:

(1) Limited access, unless you're looking for hunting rifles. Some fixers might have access to military gear, but it's doubtful.

(2) Anything other than standard loads are as rare as hen's teeth, including calibers not normally used for hunting (e.g.,.303 is easy to get, 7.52mm is a bitch).

(3) Silencers, smartgun rigs, and smart goggles are generally unavailable without special contacts.

(4) Go to the Cascade Orks. Explosives and mining go together like orks and corruption.

(5) Only the lightest armor is legal. Anything else is limited to the military (i.e., Rangers, Coasters, Border).

(6) The S-S Amerindians don't generally go in for cyber. The only exceptions are the Rangers, but they get it installed in their own clinics. So even if you can track down the gear you want, no body shops exist to install it.

(7) The Rangers have the only military vehicles around, and they take great precautions to ensure none go missing. You might find a fixer who can acquire one for you—I don't know how and I don't want to know—but it's going to cost, chummer.]<<<<<
—The Keynesian Kid (19:27:45/2-11-52)

The major multinationals have almost no presence in the Salish-Shidhe nation. The only exception is Aztechnology, which maintains a facility in Olympia. Gaeatronics purchases most of its replacement and refit supplies from Aztechnology.

>>>>>[And you should watch the little gavotte being performed by the two companies; it's a real treat. The Big A wants some leverage over Gaeatronics because, "He who controls the power source controls all." (I saw that on an Aztechnology exec's wall, no drek.) They're constantly trying to saddle Gaeatronics with some neat tech for which there's no second source. Gaeatronics always makes sure it has a second source lined up. Big A responds by attempting to buy or at least control Gaeatronics' second source. Gaeatronics counters by finding a third alternate source. The Salish aren't dumb, but José Branca, the Big A exec who came up with the "hose Gaeatronics" plan, assumed they were. He's already cost the company multi-million nuyen, and he can't admit that his ploy isn't working, so he'll keep throwing good money after bad. When the higher-ups finally tumble to what's going on, that sorry bleeder would do well to ask the Salish-Shidhe Council for political asylum and a job at Gaeatronics! Sure as drek he knows as much about where Gaeatronics gets its parts as Gaeatronics itself.]<<<<<
—Pyramid Watcher (15:39:04/4-2-52)

>>>>>[And the kid comes through again! Mr. José Branca, formerly Managing Director of Aztechnology's Olympia facility, now works as Assistant Head of Gaeatronics' Procurement Department.]<<<<<
—Pyramid Watcher (06:56:20/8-9-52)

GOVERNMENT

The tribes of the Salish-Shidhe nation are self-governing. All but the smallest have a representative on the Salish-Shidhe Council. The Council does not function like a true government. It is more a forum for arbitrating differences between the constituent tribes and a means for differing interests to contribute to an overall policy for the region. The Council has no disciplinary powers over any member tribe. Tribes can leave the Council at any time. By so doing, they save the money normally paid for upkeep of Council Island and the military forces, but they also relinquish any voice in policy-making.

In fact, policy-making privileges are the only lever the Council has available if they want to take disciplinary action against a member tribe. Any tribe that fails to pay its contribution toward the Council's "overhead" (Council Island, the military, and so on) is expelled from the Council and has no vote on any issue until all arrears have been made up. This sanction has rarely been used, because most tribes recognize the importance of having a voice in Council decisions.

The major policy decisions made by the Council concern the nation's relationships with Seattle and the nation's (sometimes shaky) relationship with the UCAS.

Currently, the major representatives on the Council are:

Salish	Harold Gray Bear
Sinsearach	Lady Gillian Morningsong
Makah	George Lodgepole
Cascade Crow	Frederick Eye-Like-Eagle
Cascade Ork	Pawl Shaggy Mountain
Nootka	Derek Darkcloud

>>>>>[I'll throw in a few more. These are not the largest tribes, but they are the ones who stir up the most trouble on the Council.

Squamish	Harold James
Musqueam	Walter Leaping Salmon
Tsawassen	Jane Water-Like-Glass
Mount Curry	Martin Tall Tree]<<<<<

—Holly (00:58:43/12-3-52)

Usually, the chief of the tribe is also the representative to the Council. Some tribes, however, select a separate representative. The procedure for selecting a chief or representative varies widely from tribe to tribe and can be decided by general consensus or by heritage.

Meetings of the Council are officially structured by rules combining various tribal traditions with Roberts' Rules of Order. In practice, meetings often degenerate into arguments. Some tales claim that Council meetings have broken down into fistfights, though these rumors have never been substantiated.

Council meetings take place once a month, usually on the day of the new moon. Extraordinary sessions can be called at any time, with 72-hour notice required. Most Council meetings are held in the Friendship Lodge in downtown Bellingham, the nation's nominal capital. Extraordinary sessions can be (and are) convened most anywhere, however. Recently, many important meetings have been held on Council Island.

>>>>>[Bellingham's a weird place. It used to be a sleepy port town—I'm talking in the 1980s here—its harbor almost totally silted up and the town itself nearly forgotten. During the Chaos, though, when Bad Things were happening in Vancouver and Seattle, the Port of Bellingham was rediscovered. The harbor was dredged and it became a boomtown. When the S-S nation was formed, it faded once again. Most capitals are bustling, high-energy places, but not Bellingham.]<<<<<
—Rackley (05:34:18/2-4-52)

COUNCIL ISLAND

Council Island (formerly Mercer Island), in the middle of Lake Washington, is the site of the Salish-Shidhe Council's embassy to Seattle. A beautiful, wooded spot, it is reminiscent of the way the land must have been centuries ago. Most buildings on the island are made from—or appear to be made from—rough-hewn logs. The island's permanent population is around 3,000 residents, but this can increase by up to 50 percent with the daily influx of tourists.

>>>>>[The ambassador to Seattle and Chief of Council Island is currently Jon Moses, seconded by Lady Laura Drywell of the Wenatchee Elf tribe, one of the smaller but more influential tribes. Jon is a good, solid type stuck in a potentially nasty job: mediating between Schultz and crew, and the S-S Council. So far, he's done an excellent job, successfully communicating the concerns of each side to the other and generally smoothing ruffled feathers.]<<<<<
—Holly (13:41:29/1-18-52)

>>>>>[I don't know whether it's Jon Moses' fault, or just a sign of the changing times, but bad feelings are starting to grow among both the S-S Amerindians and the Seattle inhabitants. I'm not saying the two governments are on the outs, in fact, they seem to be getting on as well as they ever did. It's the people. Racism against Amerindians and elves is on the rise in the city, and younger natives are starting to talk more about "solving the Seattle problem once and for all." I don't like the buzz I'm picking up.]<<<<<
—Link (21:54:31/7-18-52)

>>>>>[Jon Moses has done an outstanding job. He was a pragmatist when pragmatism was needed. But now our nation requires a harder edge when dealing with Seattle. Jon Moses doesn't have that edge, or he is unwilling to use it. Chief Moses should step down and make way for the New Wave.]<<<<<
—Wenatchee Warrior (14:26:54/8-6-52)

>>>>>[Council Island, specifically Passport Lodge, is where you arrange for visas and travel permits to travel through the native lands.]<<<<<
—Tourists' Aid (12:42:17/10-19-52)

LAWS

IMMIGRATION

The Salish-Shidhe nation is moderately open to immigration of other tribal peoples. Amerindian citizens of other NAN nations can obtain Immigrant Status with very little paperwork. Applications for Immigrant Status can be made electronically or in person at any Salish-Shidhe embassy, but must be accompanied by proof of NAN citizenship and tribal affiliation.

The situation is quite different for non-Amerindians. A prospective immigrant must be sponsored either by a Salish-Shidhe-based company that wishes to employ him or her or by a recognized tribe. In both cases, the sponsoring group must apply to the Council bureaucracy for Immigrant Status on behalf of the candidate. Though the paperwork and red tape involved are minimal, especially when compared to the immigration process in other nations, few companies or tribes go to the trouble except for exceptional individuals.

Immigration into pinkskin tribes is not as common. When the nation was formed, the government decided to oust all non-natives. Several small groups of Anglos, however, petitioned the Council for the right to stay and form their own tribes, which would be officially registered with the Council. Most of these petitions were denied, but some groups were granted tribal status. As registered tribes, these pinkskin groups also have the right to sponsor potential immigrants. However, very few of these pinkskin immigration applications are granted.

>>>>>[Far fewer than the applications made by other tribes. Indicates a severe cultural bias in a group that boasts about its even-handedness, wouldn't you say?]<<<<<
—Drek Disturber (20:16:54/1-26-52)

>>>>>[Pinkskins breed like rabbits. They're building their own numbers up quite fast enough without letting them import their mothers, fathers, uncles, aunts, etc. etc. drek etc.]<<<<<
—Wenatchee Warrior (23:10:23/6-10-52)

>>>>>[Careful, WW, your bigotry's showing.]<<<<<
—Taser (06:07:01/6-30-52)

After three years of uninterrupted residence in the Salish-Shidhe nation, a person holding Immigrant Status can apply for citizenship. A prerequisite for citizenship is membership in a registered tribal group. This is only a problem if the immigrant was initially sponsored by a company rather than a tribe. Tribes are very selective about who they accept as members, even as honorary members for the purposes of citizenship.

>>>>>[With the exception of the Cascade Ork. The orks will sometimes sell honorary tribal membership or trade it for services rendered.]<<<<<
—Hatchetman (13:14:53/8-22-52)

>>>>>[Lies.]<<<<<
—Pawl Shaggy Mountain (07:10:38/8-29-52)

DEPARTMENT OF IMMIGRATION ▶

NELSON

>>>>>[Sorry, Pawl old chummer, check your tribal seat database. You'll see I'm a registered member-in-good-standing of the Cascade Ork tribe. I received that not-so-singular honor because I helped a gang of your leg-breakers acquire some cargo from a rigger who—after we were through with him—had no further use for it. Does that ring a bell?]<<<<<
—Hatchetman (13:28:49/9-1-52)

The Salish-Shidhe nation does not issue work visas. Only those with Immigrant Status or full citizenship may work within their borders.

Tourists are welcome in the Salish-Shidhe nation.

>>>>>[...in some areas, at least.]<<<<<
—People Watcher (21:12:30/6-6-52)

In fact, certain tribes—most notably the Salish and Sinsearach—depend on tourism as a major source of income for their economy. Tourists who want to travel into the nation must have a valid passport file on their credstick. In addition, they must apply for a tourist visa and a travel permit. The visa is loaded onto the credstick. The travel permit is a blue badge that must be worn prominently at all times. Failure to wear the permit is punishable by fines. Illegal entry into the nation—in other words, being within the borders without a valid passport, visa, or travel permit—is a serious felony, punishable by heavy fines or imprisonment.

The nation's border integrity, especially with regard to illegal immigrants, is maintained by the Border and Coast Patrols. These two paramilitary organizations are well-trained and well-equipped, and make up for their relatively small numbers by using state-of-the-art passive and active sensors.

>>>>>[Border posts are manned by the Border Patrol. The guys who check you at the airports or who look through your car always seem to be friendly, good-ol'-boy types, with no armor and packing nothing heavier than a medium pistol. What you don't see are the good-ol'-boy's buddies in the back room. All border posts have a detachment of at least ten fully armed and armored Border Patrol: light to medium armor, SMGs (at least), grenades, and so on, and so on. Major crossing points are also supported by an armored vehicle and usually a couple of choppers. Don't underestimate these guys. Ditto for the Coast Patrol, but they go in for well-armed Riverines and even more choppers.]<<<<<
—Wolverine (12:50:32/10-13-52)

>>>>>[Copy that, Wolverine. The TOE lists the two Patrols as distinct from the Ranger Forces, but that's not the way it really is. The personnel are distinct—you don't get transferred from one to the other—but they undergo basic together and have at least two combined training exercises each year. What does that mean? The Patrols have less of an edge than the Rangers, but they're no slouches. Chrome is rare among the Patrol members, but the Rangers have no reservations about enhancing their skills that way. (More on that later.)]<<<<<
—Hangfire (23:42:55/10-20-52)

The area around Seattle is patrolled by the Salish-Shidhe Ranger Forces. They are responsible for manning all crossing points into and out of Seattle and patrolling the border of the "Seattle enclave." The Rangers are a full-fledged military organization. In addition to their border duties, they are also responsible for Salish-Shidhe national defense.

>>>>>[Okay, here it is. The Rangers are truly drek-hot. Not quite as sharp as the Sioux Special Forces "Wildcats," but damn near. (I remember a war game that the Sioux and S-S put on back in 2047, Rangers vs. Wildcats. The 'Cats went into it cocky as drek, expecting a cakewalk. No way, chummer. It was probably the toughest fight the 'Cats had ever been in. They won it, but barely. The Rangers came within about 5 percent of having the winning point total. Nobody—but *nobody*—has ever come that close to the 'Cats before. The Sioux command commended the S-S Rangers who took part in the game by making them honorary members of the Wildcats. The Rangers' command allows those so honored to wear a Wildcat unit designation patch on their uniforms below their own shoulderflash. (Watch out for the Rangers with the cat's-head flash. They know more ways to kill you than there are to die.) They've got the best gear and they know how to use it. Small unit tactics are supplemented by the MSX-Cray SUBTAL (Small Unit Battlefield Tactics Adviser Link) computer system, reputed to be the best battlefield Expert System unit ever designed. (Even the UCAS doesn't have the SUBTAL yet, and they want it real bad.)]<<<<<
—Hangfire (23:55:56/10-20-52)

>>>>>[The Coast and Border Patrols and the Ranger Forces are under the jurisdiction of the Salish tribe, though all other Council tribes contribute to their upkeep. The majority of military personnel is Salish, but most Council tribes are at least represented. The upper ranks are exclusively Salish, however. Even though the Council controls the forces in theory, there is some concern in other nations about the fact that the military power of the nation is dominated by the Salish.]<<<<<
—Holly (20:51:10/10-21-52)

CIVIL AND TRIBAL LAWS

The Salish-Shidhe nation has two distinct legal systems. The first is for citizens and other tribe members and is as diverse as the nations' economies. Each tribe has a body of law and custom that is binding upon the members of that tribe and anyone within that tribe's jurisdiction. Jurisdiction is usually defined as an area within a certain distance of the tribal seat. Jurisdiction varies according to the size of the tribe. Enforcing the law and dispensing justice is the responsibility of the individual tribe, and the methods of carrying out that responsibility are as unique as each group.

At one end of the scale, the Salish and Makah have official civil police forces and Judiciary Councils like those used in many other NAN nations. At the other end of the spectrum, the Musqueam tribe has no need for a police force or judiciary body. Anyone found breaking a tribal law is simply ostracized by the rest of the tribe. Tribes such as the Cascade Ork fall somewhere in the middle, presided over by a tribal council that designates certain tribe members to apprehend perpetrators.

>>>>>[In other words, the cops are the chief's hand-picked bullyboys, and the chief and his sycophants dispense "justice." Just wonderful.]<<<<<
—Hatchetman (16:39:02/7-16-52)

Tribal laws are based heavily on tribal traditions. Public drunkenness is acceptable in some tribes, in others it is against the law. In the case of social mores, particularly marriage, what is illegal according to the laws of one tribe is occasionally required by the laws of another. Visitors to the Salish-Shidhe nation should take extra care to determine the laws of each region.

Individual tribes may choose to turn over criminal suspects they apprehend to the civil judiciary body. This is common practice when the offender is a tourist, illegal immigrant, or member of another tribe.

The second legal system is the civil (as opposed to tribal) judiciary system or body. Designed to handle national laws, those put in place by the Council, rather than by individual tribes, the civil judiciary system dispenses justice to non-tribal perpetrators. The few existing national laws relate to possession of heavy weapons and cyberware, homicide, and assault. On issues that could be considered arbitrary, the Council promulgates no laws at all. For example, different tribes have different attitudes toward theft and bribery. National laws also apply to interaction with the national government and military forces. Thus, bribing a government official is against national law, as is possession of military equipment or supplies. Immi-

gration and trade regulations are also administered at the national level.

The individual tribal police forces or their equivalents are responsible for apprehending those who break national laws within tribal jurisdictions. National suspects must, by law, be handed over to the civil judiciary system. The Coast and Border Patrols and the Ranger Forces are also authorized to arrest anyone suspected of breaking a national law. They are not authorized to detain individuals suspected of breaking an exclusively tribal law, however.

Each city or large town in the Salish-Shidhe nation has at least one national Judiciary Council. This comprises either three or five judges, one of whom must be a shaman. The Council uses a legal process similar to the adversarial system of the UCAS. The Judicial Council judges, however, have greater flexibility in determining how a case will be tried. Convictions can be appealed, in theory, up to the level of the Salish-Shidhe Council itself, but very few decisions are overturned.

>>>>>[S-S law is tougher on weapons and homicide convictions than Seattle law. Fines and prison terms are typically 25 percent larger and longer than their Seattle equivalents. Otherwise, punishments are about what you'd expect.]<<<<<
—Legal Beagle (20:18:40/7-22-52)

>>>>>[The judges on a Judiciary Council never belong to the tribe in whose territory the Council sits. I believe this is supposed to minimize conflict of interest.]<<<<<
—Holly (06:57:28/12-27-52)

>>>>>[As far as I know, no judges come from the Cascade Ork tribe. That's because the Cascade Ork is one of those tribes where bribery is an expected "social lubricant." Someone from such a culture can hardly be expected to act as an objective judge.]<<<<<
—People Watcher (12:18:07/12-30-52)

Council Island jurisdiction is a special, rather troublesome case. While nominally Salish-Shidhe land, the island is physically within the Seattle enclave. The Council Island Police force is small but well-equipped and efficient. It has a working arrangement with Lone Star in greater Seattle that allows it to call up Lone Star for assistance at any time. Naturally, the CI police prefer to handle matters themselves, and so calls to Lone Star are rare.

The real problem with Council Island jurisdiction arises once a perpetrator has been apprehended. Where and how should the perpetrator be tried? If the suspect is a Salish-Shidhe citizen, he or she is simply shipped out of the Seattle enclave for trial by a nearby Judiciary Council, which is usually Olympia. It is important to note that *all* infractions committed on Council Island are handled as infractions of national law.

The situation changes when the perpetrator is a UCAS citizen from Seattle. In such a case, the Seattle government requires that the suspect be turned over to Lone Star for processing through the UCAS justice system.

>>>>>[Sure, Seattle insists, but the CIP does not always go along. A few years ago, a Seattle go-gang busted onto the island and geeked a handful of civil servants before getting nabbed. Seattle wanted them back, but the CIP told them to frag themselves. (Everyone knows how often perps skate in Seattle.) The result? Major political repercussions, and the CIP finally had to give up their prisoners (probably a little the worse for wear). And sure enough, the go-gang's lawyer found some technicality and they skated. The CIP was somewhat choked. Now this next bit isn't official by any means, but I've heard it from enough different sources to give it credence. As it stands, if someone messes up really bad on Council Island and he's caught, he just disappears. No, the CIP doesn't just geek him…though sometimes that might be a good idea. The perp is usually drugged, smuggled off the island and tried incamera, usually in Bellingham, then hauled off to jail. I don't know why the perps don't run back to Seattle and scream their heads off as soon as they're released, but so far it hasn't happened. The Seattle government hears the same rumors I do, and I'm sure they believe them…but they don't have any proof.]<<<<<
—SPD (03:35:46/6-28-52)

>>>>>[Things might get real messy if they *got* proof, right?]<<<<<
—Anonymous (01:43:44/10-12-52)

INTERNATIONAL RELATIONS

The Salish-Shidhe Council is on good diplomatic terms with virtually every nation in North America, with two major exceptions: Tsimshian and the UCAS. Relations with Tsimshian are cool mainly because of the recent increase in the Tsimshian military presence on that nation's southern border.

>>>>>[The Council tells people that there's nothing to worry about; nonetheless, it's sent a few of its crack Ranger units up to the Prince George area for "extended training." What do you make of that?]<<<<<
—Sally (21:53:16/2-25-52)

>>>>>[This development has been duly noted and commented on in the Tsimshian file (NAN Volume 2).]<<<<<
—Rex (17:29:38/3-18-52)

Some degree of tension always exists between the Salish-Shidhe nation and the UCAS, but as of this writing, that tension seems to be at its lowest ebb.

>>>>>[Danchekker's already out of date. People on both sides of the enclave boundary are getting a mite testy, it seems to me. Oh, we're probably not going to see any flare-ups, but matters might be a touch uncomfortable for a while.]<<<<<
—Buster (13:55:11/12-20-52)

The nation has a tight trading pact with the California Free State, and through them with Japan. Trade volumes are low, but both parties find the tariff-free arrangement beneficial.

>>>>>[Since the Rangers-Wildcats wargame in 2047, the S-S and Sioux have been exchanging military information and intelligence and doing some cross-training.]<<<<<
—Hangfire (23:55:56/10-20-52)

GENERAL COMMENTS

For the past several years, a vigorous argument has been running through the academic community as to whether or not the Salish-Shidhe Council and Seattle have reached a point of stability. Those who believe the system to be stable point to Berlin during the middle to second half of the 20th century as an example of a similar working relationship. The nay-sayers claim that Berlin is not directly analogous, because the two halves of Berlin were almost equal in military strength and nuclear capabilities. Neither factor applies to the Seattle and Salish-Shidhe situation.

>>>>>[There's some pressure within the nation to turn the S-S Council into something stronger: give it some teeth and use it to forge the individual tribes into a united nation. While the Salish, Makah, and even the Sinsearach support this, virtually every other tribe on the Council votes against the motion every time it's made. I can't say why for sure, but I assume it's because they fear a stronger Council will change their way of life too much.]<<<<<
—Holly (15:28:00/8-5-52)

>>>>>[The Cascade Ork vote against it because they know a Council with real disciplinary powers would take away their illegal sources of income.]<<<<<
—Vic (11:04:54/9-1-52)

SIOUX NATION

FACTS AT A GLANCE

Population: 31,810,000

Human:	70%
Elf:	6%
Dwarf:	3%
Ork:	15%
Troll:	5%
Other:	1%

Per Capita Income: 22,000¥
Below Poverty Level: 20%
On Fortune's Active Traders List: 1%
Corporate Affiliation: 31%
Education:
High School Equivalency: 55%
College Equivalency: 26%
Advanced Studies Certificates: 9%
Regional Telecom Grid Access: NA/NAN/SN

CLIMATE

The Sioux nation covers what once was the midwestern part of the United States. Much of the area has the range of temperatures typical of plains regions. It is difficult, however, to generalize about the weather in the Sioux nation because climates range considerably from one part of the nation to another.

Winter temperatures often drop well below zero while summer temperatures can exceed 37 degrees Celsius. Each region has a different average annual rainfall. Tornados are a seasonal event, though few cause significant damage. While some funnel storms move north and west through the CAS from the Gulf of Mexico or the Atlantic, many form in the plains regions themselves.

>>>>>[Danchekker doesn't have the cojones to say it straight out, but the weather system throughout this region is just plain fragged. It's as difficult to make a two-day forecast here as it is to run a five-day forecast for other parts of the continent. I admit I don't know why this is. Theories include uneven global warming, disruption of the jet streams by suborbital and semiballistic traffic, even the effects of thermal plumes from fusion reactors. The moral of this little tale is to pack your bikini *and* your parka, remember your rain gear, and reserve your storm shelter in advance.]<<<<<
—Woppler the Weatherman (10:24:22/4-4-52)

>>>>>[The theory I give most credence to is that the sometimes freakish weather across NAN (and it is concentrated there, though most, including Danchekker, won't admit it) is the aftereffect of Howling Coyote's Great Ghost Dance. Nothing comes without its price, chummers.]<<<<<
—Simone (10:45:23/5-14-52)

ACCESS

Plane

The Sioux nation's largest international airport is not in Cheyenne, the capital, but in Casper. In fact, Cheyenne Airport is classed as international only because the city is so close to the borders of the Ute and Pueblo nations.

Casper offers regularly scheduled suborbital and semiballistic service to most major cities around the world. In contrast, Cheyenne only offers regular flights to Salt Lake City, Lincoln, Denver, and Topeka.

The Sioux nation has more licensed independent short-hop carriers than any other country in North America. As of this writing, the Sioux government authorizes some 60 carriers. The largest are Table Top Travel, Skybus, Skycab, Eagle Feather Transit, and Bonnie's.

>>>>>[Many companies equals too few inspections. The Sioux nation has short-hop carriers falling out of the sky on a regular basis. Some of these accidents are mid-air collisions and some are the result of spontaneous equipment failure, but most are caused by pilot error.]<<<<<
—Right Stuff (02:26:36/1-8-52)

>>>>>[The government keeps talking about creating a centralized control system, similar to Pueblo's Airlink, but the independent carriers are fighting it every step of the way.]<<<<<
—Tony (02:28:20/3-18-52)

Automobile or Bus

Major surface routes into the Sioux nation include Highway 90, leading southeast from Butte (Algonkian-Manitoo Council), Highway 25 from Denver, Route 80 from Omaha (UCAS), and the western continuation of Route 80 from Salt Lake City and Ogden (Ute nation). Whippet Bus Lines and Screaming Eagle Overland both offer regular service along these routes. Sioux National Transit runs a local service between Cheyenne and Casper.

>>>>>[Riding an SNT bus is an experience, chummer. I think the drivers are all ex-panzer riggers, because they drive like they're expecting to take heavy fire at any moment. Use the seat belts and try not to use the can.]<<<<<
—Chilled in Cheyenne (21:08:03/7-5-52)

TRIBAL DEMOGRAPHICS

The Sioux nation boasts more distinct tribes in its membership than any other NAN nation. Twelve main tribes represent all but 1 percent of the population. These percentages break down as follows:

Sioux	18%
Crow	12%
Navaho	12%
Hidatsa	10%
Arapaho	10%
Cree	8%
Plains Chippewa	8%
Blackfoot	7%
Apache	7%
Cheyenne	4%
Mohawk	3%
Other	1%

Very few residents of the Sioux nation are unable to claim native ancestry. All non-natives are immigrants, Anglos working in the high-technology sector and congregated around Cheyenne. Non-natives with full citizenship are respected for their value to the nation and enjoy all the official benefits of any Sioux citizen. In general, however, non-natives are held in low regard.

>>>>>[Sioux residents do not easily accept Anglos. But once you've earned their respect, they'll stand behind you no matter how tough the going gets. For a tough op, I'd rather have the Sioux at my back than anyone else.]<<<<<
　　—Mad Merc (18:00:37/3-22-52)

Representation in government is determined by the ratio of tribal population to total population. The Sioux ruling council adheres almost exactly to this proportion. The Apache tribe receives slightly higher representation than allowed by this formula, but no obvious friction exists between the members of the different tribes.

The civil service, on the other hand, shows a clear division of responsibilities based on tribal origin. The police force is almost exclusively Cheyenne, while the nation's armed forces are largely Cree and Mohawk. The civil service bureaus dedicated to delivering social services are mainly Hidatsa. When the Sioux nation was originally formed, these divisions were created by mutual agreement between the tribes. Though the agreements were never given the force of law, this functional segregation continues. Those who have attempted to analyze this division of labor speculate that the system is based on an assumption that the members of any tribe will be more comfortable surrounded by others of similar backgrounds and traditions.

>>>>>[If the tribes aren't "encouraged" to stick to their own job pool, then why have no Crow, Navaho, or Blackfoot applicants ever been accepted into the civil police force, hm?]<<<<<
　　—Rolling Thunder (06:08:38/3-28-52)

>>>>>[Possibly because the applicants weren't officer material. According to my research, the majority of non-Cheyenne applicants to the police force applied *solely* as an attempt to break what they saw as the stranglehold one tribe had on the force. That doesn't strike me as a good recommendation for a potential cop.]<<<<<
　　—People Watcher (07:50:37/3-30-52)

While the Sioux nation as a whole has not aggressively returned to the traditions of its heritage, one tradition has been widely resurrected. The sign language developed by the Plains Indians in the 18th century for inter-tribal communication is enjoying renewed popularity. This language of gestures is complex, efficient, fluid, and quite beautiful to watch. Unlike many forms of sign language, it is not based on limited vocabulary. People sufficiently fluent in the language can easily discuss philosophical and ethical concepts as well as concrete matters such as the weather.

>>>>>[I've worked with a number of Plains tribes on various, um, assignments, and their sign language can be a lifesaver in combat situations. I've seen highly complex instructions relayed in total silence under conditions of complete EMCON as fast or faster than I could send them over a comnet. Impressive as hell, chummer. I've tried to learn it myself, but I'm far from fluent.]<<<<<
　　—Mad Merc (18:03:52/3-22-52)

>>>>>[EMCON?]<<<<<
　　—Fader (19:54:59/3-22-52)

>>>>>[EMission CONtrol. Radio silence, drek-head.]<<<<<
　　—Mad Merc (05:30:07/4-1-52)

>>>>>[Next time you're in Cheyenne, check out the Sioux National Theater (near Pershing and 23rd). Every year, they perform at least two shows exclusively in sign language. It's almost like watching ballet and a real treat if you know the play. I saw *Of Mice and Men*, and it was quite an experience.]<<<<<
　　—Holly (08:22:35/4-8-52)

>>>>>[I don't know if it's a new development, but young men in the Sioux nation show intensely macho, ultramasculine behavior. Threat and counterthreat seem to be the main forms of interpersonal communication between strangers within this subculture. It appears to be very ritualistic, however, rarely resulting in physical fighting. In this way, it resembles the threat-dominance-submission behavior in wolves. This behavior can cause trouble when different subcultures mix. A couple of months back, there was damn near an all-out war in a Casper bar (the Flame Tavern, if you know Casper at all). As it was told to me, a couple of out-of-nation razorguys came in for a drink and some of the locals showed their teeth. The runners took it to be a genuine threat and responded accordingly: hard option. It was an instant replay of Custer's Last Stand. The final score: two razorguys and four locals geeked, twelve locals badly scragged. It also created some serious tension for the next few weeks.]<<<<<
　　—Socio Pat (21:17:02/7-5-52)

▼ ▼ ▼ ▼ ▼ ▼ ▼

>>>>>[If you look closer, you'll find that behavior concentrated heavily in the Mohawk tribe. But it ties in with a strong national interest in violent, aggressive sports. Some South American nations obsess over soccer. In a similar way, members of the Sioux nation obsess over urban brawl, combat biking, and similar just-fragging-charming creations of their own.]<<<<<
—People Watcher (06:36:43/7-21-52)

>>>>>[Going back to Socio Pat's comments: It's an interesting fact that few go-gangs and thriller-gangs run on the streets of the Sioux nation. The few that do exist have an older membership and seem to be left over from earlier days.]<<<<<
—NFA (22:29:36/8-15-52)

HISTORY AND CULTURE

The majority of the Sioux nation tribes originated in the plains region of North America. Of the twelve main tribes, only the Mohawk immigrated to the area. They come from the Eastern Woodlands along with several other tribes including the Delaware, Onondaga, Oneida, Mahican, Mohegan, Cherokee, and Choctaw. These groups are only remnants of once-mighty tribes and make up less than 1 percent of the nation's population.

The Eastern Woodlands tribes were the first to encounter European settlers and explorers. At first, relations between the two cultural groups were friendly, but the peace did not last. Soon the settlers and the Amerindians were engaged in running warfare. The settlers moved westward, taking the land for their own and paying for it in blood.

By the early 1800s, Europeans had reached the Mississippi River. As they continued to seek "unclaimed" land in the west, the settlers negotiated peace treaties with the Indians.

>>>>>[Most of which the Anglos quickly broke, frag them.]<<<<<
—Squanto (14:54:33/4-10-52)

In 1830, Congress passed the Indian Removal Act, which granted the government the right to move the remaining Woodlands Amerindians west of the Mississippi. Their reservations were soon interspersed with those set up for the Plains tribes. The Plains tribes fought fiercely against the European incursion, but inevitably lost.

The tribes that would join together in the Sioux nation were almost all early members of SAIM, and later NAN. Several of the tribes joined the Plains Federation, a group autonomous from but allied with SAIM and NAN, which was disbanded in 2011. Except for a few firebrands, most of the tribes had accepted that a united front under the SAIM/NAN banner would be more effective than a piecemeal approach.

>>>>>[I was one of Danchekker's "firebrands," and I'm proud of it. Look at what SAIM and NAN have given us. The Sioux nation could be a proud state, emblematic of what made the Plains nations strong in the days of our forefathers. Instead, it's bound by some outmoded council to seal-hunters and cliff-dwellers who have no sense of honor. I spit on NAN and the STC. And I will do what I can to bring about its fall.]<<<<<
—Proud Son (17:15:26/5-29-52)

>>>>>[Suck dried lizard drek, you fossil.]<<<<<
—Pueblo Princess (04:42:17/6-8-52)

Because the Eastern Woodlands tribes comprise such a small proportion of its population, the attitudes and mores of the Sioux nation are largely those of the Plains Amerindians. Their sense of honor is strong: to insult the ancestry or heritage of a Sioux citizen is to commit an unforgivable offense.

The Sioux nation bound the disparate tribes with a call to brotherhood, dividing the duties and responsibilities of nationhood among all members.

>>>>>[Drek, chummer. Call to brotherhood? More like the only compromise that would keep the tribes from each others' throats.]<<<<<
—Jerboa (18:15:44/2-10-52)

Among the Plains tribes, traditional dress is deerskin breechcloths, leggings, moccasins, and undecorated shirts. A small minority wear the traditional costume on a daily basis, but it is mostly worn on ceremonial occasions.

The Eastern Woodlands tribes seem to have had a significant effect on the religious rituals practiced in the Sioux nation. Two secret societies of shamans, the Midewiwin Society and the False Face Society, are still active. Plains tribesmen are welcomed as members of the societies, but no outsider has been able to discover their purpose.

>>>>>[Lazy, Danchekker. Researchers like you are supposed to *find out* what goes on in these things. Anybody out there have any info?]<<<<<
   —Ross (14:18:49/3-21-52)

>>>>>[Historically, both the Midewiwin and the False Face were curing societies, dedicated to healing the injured and the sick. The Midewiwin based their healing ceremonies on special songs, while the FFS members wore ugly wooden masks while performing their rituals. I assume they're into the same kind of thing today. Now that magic's returned to the world, their rituals are probably a lot more effective.]<<<<<
   —Holly (21:26:48/4-2-52)

>>>>>[The False Faces have discarded their masks. The shamans' power transforms them enough that the masks have become redundant.]<<<<<
   —Many-Names (23:59:59/4-10-52)

>>>>>[This is just a rumor and I'm not saying it's the truth—but here's something interesting. From what I've heard, the Midewiwin Society has changed its focus from curing individual sicknesses to curing the sickness in the Sioux nation as a whole. According to the rumors, the Midewiwins have become shamanic vigilantes, waging a private war on the BTL industry, the Mafia, and anyone else who appears to be harming the Sioux way of life. Don't quote me on this. (And if there are any Midewiwins out there, don't geek me, 'kay?)]<<<<<
   —Alias (17:58:11/6-10-52)

A TRIBE IN PERSPECTIVE: THE MOHAWK

The Mohawk tribe was part of the Iroquois federation, or Five Nations. Formed in about 1570 under the leadership of Hiawatha and Dekanawida, the Iroquois federation comprised the Mohawk, Oneida, Onondaga, Cayuga, and Seneca tribes. In 1722, the Tuscarora joined the federation, which occupied the upper portion of what used to be New York State (now part of UCAS).

The Mohawks had a reputation as fierce fighters. They and the other Iroquois tribes obtained firearms from Dutch settlers in the early 1600s and subdued all the tribes from the St. Lawrence River to Tennessee and from Maine to Michigan in no time at all. They held total control over the fur trade, and allowed only those canoes whose owners paid a tribute to pass through the Great Lakes.

Under leaders such as Joseph Brant, the Iroquois federation sided with the British against the French. The federation split, however, over the question of who to support in the Revolutionary War. The Mohawks chose to support the British and suffered for their choice at the hands of the Americans after the war. The majority of the Mohawk tribe moved north to reservations in Canada.

The Mohawks lived quietly until Indian land claims became controversial again in the late 1980s and early 1990s. The Mohawks supported their land claim by blockading roads into a reservation just south of the Canadian border. The blockades were quickly dismantled by the U.S. Army. Several months later, the Mohawks blockaded a bridge leading into Oka, Québec. This time their actions led to a week-long stand-off that was punctuated by violent clashes between Mohawk warriors and Canadian soldiers. Once again, the Mohawk warriors were forced to back down and the blockades were dismantled.

Almost a decade later, the Canadian Mohawks blocked roads leading into their reservations around Oka, Kahnawake, and Kanesatake in Québec. They declared themselves the Sovereign Mohawk Nation. While the world watched, the Canadian government hesitated. The total population of the "Nation" was no more than 5,000, and only 500 of those were actually Mohawk warriors. The tactical situation was more complex than it seemed, however.

>>>>>[Damn right it was. I was there, boys, just a snot-nosed 18-year-old Canadian Armed Forces recruit in my nice green uniform with my nice new automatic rifle. Almost a thousand of us faced off against maybe 500 Mohawk warriors. A rabble armed with melon knives and hunting rifles, right? *Wrong.* The rumors we heard said the Mohawks had connections with some pretty heavy-duty terrorist groups and they'd stockpiled serious ordnance. RPGs, claymores, grenade launchers, and lots of crew-served .50-cals. (Ever faced a 1999-vintage mil-spec .50-cal, boys and girls? Stand in the middle of a downtown city block and look around you. Nothing you see will stop a .50-cal round. The "cover" will just tumble the round for you. Nice, eh?) The Mohawks were dug into fortified positions and probably had laid mines around the choke points. The big question was did they have anti-air weaponry—Stingers or Gremlins? That question was what made us hesitate.]<<<<<
—Dennis Peet (18:08:42/10-3-52)

After a four-week stand-off, the army made its move. Initial army losses were high. The first-assault infantry was unable to dislodge the Mohawks. The second assault included armor with close air support. The Mohawk position was weakened, but the warriors still held one well-fortified position in Kahnawake. Before the third and final assault, the Canadian forces offered safe-conduct to noncombatants. Their offer was ignored. On the morning of October 3, 1999, precisely at local dawn, a perfect time-on-target salvo of Cataphract wire-guided missiles hit on the Kahnawake fortification. Mechanized infantry, an armored platoon, and several air cav units moved in and the fighting was over by noon. The Sovereign Mohawk Nation was completely wiped out.

After the destruction of the Sovereign Mohawk Nation, the Canadian government took steps to ensure that the Mohawk tribe would not stage a repeat performance. All Mohawks were moved from other reservations to a "Protection Center" near Swift Current, Saskatchewan. The government justified this move by claiming it was necessary to "protect" the surviving Mohawks against retribution, by other tribes and Anglos alike, for the Kahnawake incident. In an unprecedented and unexpected move, the United States government relocated the Mohawks on American reservations to the Canadian internment camp as well. The total Mohawk population had dropped to only 25,000. Surrounded by high fences and guarded by the Canadian army, the Mohawks had no chance to become involved in the actions of SAIM until Canada finally disintegrated.

Freed from the Protection Center, the Mohawks moved south. Their historical territory was now part of UCAS, and so the few surviving Mohawks petitioned for entry and were accepted into the newly formed Sioux nation.

The Mohawks make up in fierce pride what they lack in numbers, and have gained a significant voice in the Sioux nation's government. All members of the Mohawk tribe are instructed, almost from birth, in their tragic history. They are determined that, as a people, they will never allow such oppression again. The vast majority of Mohawks, both male and female, proclaim their ancestry by wearing the traditional "mohawk" hairstyle. Few, however, have adopted the breech-cloth and leggings of their ancestors.

>>>>>[Gotcha, Danchekker! There's an error in the last 'graph, and it serves as a perfect example of how even people as (supposedly) close to their culture and history as the Mohawks can let things slip with time and get diverted by often erroneous "conventional wisdom." Sure, the hairstyle with a crest, or fringe, on top and the rest of the scalp shaved is called the "mohawk." But it was the Creek, Powhatan, and Chickasaw tribes (from the same region as the Mohawks) who wore that style. The other Iroquois tribes, including the Mohawks, shaved the *top* of the head, leaving a fringe around the edges.]<<<<<
—Holly (18:52:23/2-27-52)

>>>>>[Where do you get your info, Anglo?]<<<<<
—Hiawatha (04:10:01/5-3-52)

ECONOMY

The Sioux nation economic structure is an interesting juxtaposition of two subeconomies. One is largely agrarian, heavily assisted by high technology; the other is mainly tertiary (information processing) industry. The small amount of secondary (manufacturing-based) industry is very clean. The Sioux nation has some of the toughest anti-pollution laws in the world, and they all are strongly enforced.

The Sioux nation is North America's number one producer of genetically augmented grain crops. Many of these, including neo-triticale and stonewheat, yield up to four crops per year. Unprecedented crop densities are made possible by genetic "tailoring" that allows individual plants to grow much closer together than natural strains. Yield is increased even more by the judicious use of hydroponics, used primarily in the cultivation of soy and yeast. The Sioux nation's major export crops are grain, soy, and processed yeast protein. The government-run Advanced Pest Control Laboratory (APCL) in Laramie is known world-wide for its innovative work in targeted viral pesticides.

>>>>>[Biogene claims that APCL stole its genome for a subviral phage that geeks tobacco mosaic virus. In a countersuit, APCL claims it was Biogene who scammed the design, not the other way around. Both outfits are under injunction not to manufacture or market the phage. Meanwhile, Renraku is making a fragging mint selling its own tobacco mosaic phage—which just so happens to be genetically identical to the APCL/Biogene design. A coincidence?]<<<<<
—Chimera (23:45:32/2-3-52)

>>>>>[I happened to be wandering through both the Biogene and APCL computer systems and I made an interesting discovery. According to the documentation, it looks like a case of almost simultaneous independent discovery (which actually isn't all that rare in the sciences). Now the interesting bit: In both systems, there's unmistakable evidence of decker penetration. In other words, both companies have "proof" that the other one infiltrated their system. I can't prove it, but I think both penetrations were the work of Renraku deckers. Fun stuff, eh?]<<<<<
—FastJack (23:22:34/3-30-52)

>>>>>[Genetic engineering is a blight. Mankind has no right to tamper with what Nature has fine-tuned over millions of years. The possibility of a bio-disaster is too great for us to be blinded by the short-term advantages. No Designer Genes! Hands Off Nature!]<<<<<
—Save Our Genomes (04:38:40/4-15-52)

>>>>>[SOG? Give me a fragging break! Neo-Luddites everywhere.]<<<<<
—Technocrat (21:59:30/5-27-52)

>>>>>[What in drek's a "Luddite" anyway?]<<<<<
—Jilly (03:38:08/5-29-52)

>>>>>[The Luddites were the first techno-terrorists. In England a couple of centuries ago, they trashed a factory that was using the first form of automation. It was the cotton gin or something.]<<<<<
—Nora (09:49:41/6-6-52)

The University of Cheyenne is world-renowned for its innovative work in artificial intelligence and Expert Systems technology. More than one hundred software and hardware companies have sprung up in the Cheyenne area to develop and market products based on technology licensed from UC. Many of these products are state-of-the-art and find ready markets throughout North America and around the world. The largest of these companies is FTL Technologies, marketer of the "Warpdrive" language-translation software used in automated transaction systems world-wide.

>>>>>[FTL is a heavy hitter in the cyberdeck program market as well. If you use an off-the-shelf Fairlight or Fuchi deck, odds are your Persona code is based on an FTL development, which in turn was based on a UC breakthrough.]<<<<<
—Laser's Edge (12:39:33/6-8-52)

>>>>>[FTL hasn't spread out of Sioux yet, but it's a very big player. It just fought off a hostile takeover attempt by MCT—literally. MCT is used to playing rough, but they're not used to losing. The way I scan it, they lost an entire penetration team, physical and decker. No survivors. No scoop on FTL losses, but I'd guess they were as high.]<<<<<
—Hummer (14:40:54/7-24-52)

The Bureau of High Technology ruled in 2026 that only Sioux-based corporations were eligible to license technology from the University of Cheyenne. As of this writing, 27 challenges to this ruling still await decisions by the courts. All these challenges were made by major multinationals. The Bureau also put a 20 percent cap on foreign ownership of high-technology companies which allows them to refute charges of unfair trade practices.

>>>>>[…and you can almost hear the wailing and gnashing of teeth in skyscrapers worldwide.]<<<<<
—Tardis (02:43:52/5-17-52)

>>>>>[How does this gibe with MCT's attempted takeover?]<<<<<
—Inquiring Mind (02:27:45/7-27-52)

>>>>>[I cut the story a little short. It's an open secret in the decker community that the takeover was an MCT operation. *Officially*, MCT is separated from the fracas by three holding companies and a shell. In other words, "Hey guys, it wasn't us." Sure, chummer.]<<<<<
—Hummer (03:50:24/8-3-52)

Except where they relate to licensed University of Cheyenne discoveries, very few limits are placed on the activities of major corporations in the Sioux nation, even in the high-technology sector. All the major multinational corporations have a presence in the Sioux nation, and most have major facilities in Cheyenne, Casper, or Laramie. The most impressive of these is Mitsuhama's seven-tower complex at Collins and Wolcott in downtown Casper.

>>>>>[Going counter to tradition (see my entry under Government), the Bureau of High Technology has proven almost impossible to bribe or otherwise suborn. My contacts say that corps from Aztechnology and MCT down to Nestle are doing their best to change that. The sums being discussed are impressive, to say the least.]<<<<<
—Iris (07:17:45/10-23-52)

>>>>>[That may change soon. The buzz in the shadows is that the head of the Bureau has a son who tried his hand as a shadow decker. He tried to bust into Renraku's system in New York. Renraku security is now holding the kid and threatening to turn him over to the UCAS cops. Odds are that this situation will give Renraku the leverage they need to waive some of the more restrictive Bureau regulations.]<<<<<
—Lee (10:41:15/11-18-52)

The standard of living in the Sioux nation is close to that of Seattle. High-technology products are generally cheaper than in Seattle, but only if manufactured locally. Imported technology is at least 10 percent more expensive, because the Bureau of High Technology collects tariffs in an effort to stimulate local business development.

>>>>>[…which leads us to cost differentials. Once again, the costs given for tech toys are for those of Sioux manufacture. If you want to buy something imported, the price will usually be about 110 percent of what you'd pay in Seattle.

SIOUX COST OF LIVING	
ITEM	**COST**
Weaponry	
Ammunition	95% (1)
Explosives	110% (3)
Firearm Accessories	8% (2)
Firearms	100%
Melee Weapons	100%
Projectile Weapons	95%
Throwing Weapons	90%
Armor	
Armor	150% (4)
Surveillance and Security	
Communications	90%
Security Devices	90%
Surveillance Countermeasures	90%
Surveillance Measures	90%
Survival Gear	180% (5)
Vision Enhancers	70%
Lifestyle	
Lifestyle	120%
Electronics	
Electronics	90%
Cybertech	
Biotech	120%
Bodyware	90%
Cyberdecks	70% (7)
Headware	90% (6)
Internals	90%
Programs	90%
Magical Equipment	
Hermetic Library	200%
Magical Supplies	180%
Magical Weapons	300%
Power Foci	150%
Ritual Sorcery Materials	200%
Spell Foci	150% (8)
Vehicles	
Aircraft	130%
Boats	180%
Ground Vehicles	140%
Military Vehicles	180% (9)

Cost of Living—Notes:
    (1) Corporate security services and their designates may legally purchase the nastier forms of ordnance including APDS and explosive rounds.
    (2) Silencers are legal for corps. The Sioux nation is easygoing about smartgun links, but only their own. The only available Sioux-made link comes from Telspot and it's notoriously unreliable.
    (3) Few regulations control the sale of explosives. All you need is an easy-to-forge certificate of need and a good reason for blowing something up.

(4) Anything heavier than armored jackets is restricted to cops, army, and corp sec-guards.

(5) This one surprised even me.

(6) I personally would rather eat broken glass than put something of Sioux manufacture inside my skull. But that's probably just a personal bias.

(7) FTL puts out a really wiz deck that's almost equivalent to the Fairlight Excalibur, and its little brother is on a par with the Fuchi Cyber-6.

(8) Anything to do with magic is going to cost more than you'd expect.

(9) The government allows corp sec-forces and their legal designates to own just about anything. If you can somehow get yourself named a "legal designate" then you can be the first runner on your block to own a Citymaster.

I should explain my negative attitude about Sioux-manufactured headware. The central technology of their products is uniformly excellent: the CPUs are wiz, and the soft/firmware routines are elegant. It's the peripheral stuff, the connections that actually let the stuff interface with your nervous system, I find doubtful. One recurring rumor is that a major corp exec died when his internal telephone locked into a busy-signal feedback loop. Not a good way to go.]<<<<<
—The Keynesian Kid (17:49:02/2-11-52)

GOVERNMENT

The major governing body of the Sioux nation is the Council of Chiefs. For historical reasons, 20 chiefs serve on the council. Each major tribe in the nation must have at least one representative. Chiefs are selected by a 20-member Council of Elders, mostly shamans. All major tribes must have at least one elder on the Council.

Chiefs serve a five-year term and are appointed only once. Elders accept their positions for life. When an elder dies, a replacement is selected by the Council of Chiefs. Fifteen chiefs must agree before a candidate can be appointed to the vacant position.

This system is not democratic, but it works. The elders are free to select chiefs based on their leadership abilities, whether or not the candidates are popular with the citizens.

>>>>>[In other words, if a guy's a drek-hot administrator but has the personal magnetism of a plate of grass, he can be named to the government. That couldn't happen in a democracy.]<<<<<
—E Pluribus (17:39:20/6-4-52)

To be considered for a senior office (chief or elder), a candidate must be a native of the Sioux nation and must be able to prove direct descent from one of the nation's major tribes. Chiefs are paid an excellent salary, and so more of the elders' selections accept their nomination than might be expected.

Other governmental officials are appointed by the chiefs.

The government is divided into bureaus, each responsible for one aspect of administration. The bureaus include High Technology, Health and Welfare, Resource Management, Agriculture, Immigration and Revenue, Civil Enforcement, Justice, and National Security. Other, smaller bureaus administer lesser governmental functions. Each bureau is autonomous, answerable only to the Council of Chiefs. Bureau heads serve terms from three years (Health and Welfare) to ten years (National Security).

>>>>>[The entire governmental structure is rife with corruption. Bribery is an accepted way of expediting matters and is sometimes even acknowledged in corporations' annual reports. This corruption almost never extends into the chiefs or elders, however...or doesn't seem to. Maybe it's just that the chiefs and elders are more discreet. Only one chief has ever been caught taking graft, and she was chucked out on her ear and then brought up on charges.]<<<<<
—Iris (00:06:26/10-23-52)

Internal affairs are decided by a majority vote of the Council of Chiefs. Matters of international policy must be approved by 14 members, a two-thirds majority.

>>>>>[...which explains why the Sioux nation's international policies are stagnant. Get 14 out of 20 people, each with their own agenda, to agree on something? Give me a break.]<<<<<
—Scag (09:02:31/2-4-52)

LAWS

IMMIGRATION

Unlike other NAN nations, the Sioux nation has managed to avoid a "brain drain" among its more highly educated and trained citizens. In fact, the reputation of both the University of Cheyenne and the Laramie Advanced Pest Control Laboratory attracts some of the best minds in computer technology and genetic engineering. The nation suffers from a shortage of manual laborers, however. For this reason, the government makes it as easy as possible for prospective immigrants or even visitors to work in the nation. Citizenship or work visas are required only for employment in the high-technology sectors. (Income tax is withheld at source for even non-immigrant or transient workers, however, ensuring that the government does not lose revenue.) In the high-technology sector, the appropriate bureau levies surcharges against companies employing non-citizens. This serves as a strong incentive for such companies to give preferential employment to Sioux citizens.

Citizenship is offered immediately to prospective immigrants who can prove descent from one of the nation's major tribes. All other immigrants can apply for citizenship after three years of uninterrupted residence. During the interim period, immigrants are granted Official Resident status. Because the nation is not a democracy, very few benefits come with citizenship that are not available with Official Resident status. For this reason, many Official Residents never apply for full citizenship.

>>>>>[Danchekker claims "anyone can work." That's true if you're an Amerind, but it's not necessarily so if you're not. Oh, the official policy says otherwise, but if you're not tribal, you ain't going to get a job (sorry, chummer). Exceptions are made in the real cutting-edge high-tech jobs where the nation simply can't find the appropriate skill-set internally. But exceptions are very rare. So don't even expect to get a job wrenching on bikes unless you've got tribal ancestry.]<<<<<
—Gasket (23:31:39/1-13-52)

>>>>>[Customs officers at the border are very efficient, and have access to some seriously wiz tech to detect contraband: chemical sniffers, NMR scanners, the works. Luckily, corruption is as common among the customs service as it is in other areas of government. If you cross the right palms with silver, and do it in an acceptably subtle manner, you can import just about anything.]<<<<<
—Harley (20:00:10/5-8-52)

>>>>>[Harley makes an important point. Bribery, graft, grease, baksheesh, whatever you call it—it's a way of life. It may look like corruption, but it's circumscribed by convention and social strictures. For example, you should never mention the word "bribe" to an official. "Gifts" and "voluntary donations" to the "Customs Officials Retirement Fund" are okay. And don't try to put a "gift" on your credstick, chummer. Naturally, paying too much is just a coincidence, but the Sioux nation is one of the few that still mints cash. One, five, and ten nuyen coins are made of metallized plastic, and coated-mylar bills come in denominations up to 1K nuyen. A 500¥ note folded in your passport will soften the hardest bureaucratic heart, while offering a padded credstick

will just get you charged with attempting to bribe an official. (Credstick transactions can be traced, after all. Not so with cash.)]<<<<<
—Aunt Acid (22:22:07/7-22-52)

>>>>>[Border guards and customs officials are armed to the fragging teeth: heavy armor, medium MGs, and assault cannons are the order of the day. Crossing posts are usually supported by at least an APC (often a Citymaster) and one or more rotary-wing craft, usually Yellowjackets. The borders are long, but they're well-covered by surveillance drones, motion detectors, low-light imaging systems, and other swift tech. And those brittle-looking "wooden" barricades they have at crossing posts: they're actually high-tensile duralumin, and many of them are trapped. Ram one, and a shaped charge may burn through the front of your vehicle with unpleasant consequences.]<<<<<
—Dick Doolittle (09:16:12/9-28-52)

CIVIL AND TRIBAL LAWS

Law enforcement is the bailiwick of the Bureau of Civil Enforcement, but dispensing justice is the responsibility of the Bureau of Justice. The Bureau of Civil Enforcement, which includes the national police force, is highly efficient. It consistently out-performs the Bureau of Justice. Perpetrators often are apprehended quickly, then must wait days, weeks, or sometimes months before their cases come to trial.

>>>>>[The cops are as corrupt as they come and pretty blatant about it. Last year I got a speeding ticket in downtown Laramie...while I was waiting at a stoplight. It cost me a 50¥ donation to the Police Benevolent Fund to get on the road again.]<<<<<
—Aunt Acid (22:40:25/7-22-52)

>>>>>[Don't make the mistake of thinking they're comic-opera buffoons. Sioux cops are very efficient when they want to be and won't take a bribe in a high-profile crime. (The glory they'll get from taking you in will be worth more in the long run than any bribe you can offer them.) If a cop gets killed during the action,all bets are off. You could offer them the GNP of UCAS and they'd still blow your brains into your lap. And they've got the firepower to do it. On regular patrol they wear light armor and pack machine pistols, but when the drek gets heavy they wheel up the serious ordnance and bring in vehicular and air support.]<<<<<
—Bullseye (00:29:06/8-8-52)

Judiciary Councils roughly equivalent to our courts are presided over by a single judge. Judges are appointed by the Bureau of Justice and hold their positions for life unless removed for just cause. Prosecutors, defense counsels, and all lawyers are licensed by the Bureau of Justice.

Trials are conducted in the adversarial tradition familiar to residents of the UCAS. The judge, however, has more discretion to admit or exclude evidence and testimony than does a UCAS judge. Judges also have more freedom in interpreting laws and precedents. The Sioux nation still hands down sentences of capital punishment for offenses such as premeditated murder, often invoking the death penalty.

>>>>>[I remember going before a real ball-whacker of a judge named Mary Cat Dancing. The cops picked me up on suspicion of aggravated assault (not guilty, at least this time). Detention wasn't convenient at the moment, so I tried to run. I headed into a crowd, figuring the cops wouldn't open up if there was a chance civilians might stop some rounds. But one drek-head burned a clip my way anyway and got me in the back of my armor jacket. The impact took me down, so they got me...but a ricochet hit a bystander in the headbone and it was sayonara, over and out. Mary Cat Dancing sentenced me to the Big Trip for murdering the civilian.]<<<<<
—Anonymous (00:28:00/3-24-52)

>>>>>[Obviously she didn't, Anon, unless ghosts have data-jacks.]<<<<<
— T r u d y (00:30:56/3-24-52)

>>>>>[Oh, she sentenced me all right. Death by lethal injection (Do it to him in vein). It was my good luck that seeing me geeked wasn't convenient for my Mr. Johnson. Some of his boys broke in and hauled me out.]<<<<<
—A n o n y m o u s (00:32:01/3-24-52)

>>>>>[Mary Cat Dancing was a recent purchase of Mitsuhama. Many Sioux judges supplement their income with corporate grease. (I take it Anon's Mr. Johnson wasn't MCT.)]<<<<<
—Clean Gene (12:11:11/7-12-52)

>>>>>[Judges can be a good purchase, but the price tag is out of most runners' range. I hear Mary Cat Dancing gets a well-buried retainer of 100K+ a year, plus bonuses of a few K¥ here and there for services rendered.]<<<<<
—F9 (18:40:32/7-16-52)

>>>>>[Grafting a judge is a tricky proposition. You've got to be real slick and real oblique. And even then it's a risk. Some are straight-arrow, and they'll put you away for a good, long time just for trying.]<<<<<
—Suzy Q (17:26:08/11-27-52)

INTERNATIONAL RELATIONS

Nominally a member of the NAN, with an official representative on the Sovereign Council, the Sioux nation is generally unconcerned and uninvolved with the issues that trouble the other members of the Council. Despite their seemingly callous attitude, the nation is on good terms with all other North American nations, with the exception of Tsimshian. Even friction with this one nation is limited to personality clashes between the Council representatives.

A strong trade alliance is building between the Sioux and Pueblo nations. Before either nation will enter into a major high-technology trade agreement with another country, the two nations confer to make sure the deal benefits both. Other nations on the Sovereign Council have spoken out against this alliance as being detrimental to free trade and constituting a "tech-nocrat-monopoly" or "Western fortress." So far, complaints have been low-key and the Council shows no inclination to act on them.

The Sioux nation has good diplomatic relations with the California Free State and through them with Japan. UC has set up several exchange programs with the Nippon Institute of Technology (NIT) in Saitama. Great benefits are expected to result from this strategic alliance.

GENERAL COMMENTS

The Sioux nation has one of the largest, best-equipped, and most extensively trained militaries among the NAN nations. The nation is very sensitive about the long frontier it shares with the UCAS. It fears, probably without reason, that the UCAS will attempt to annex some of the land they "lost" in the Treaty of Denver. Members of the UCAS armed forces are not allowed into Sioux territory: even off-duty personnel are turned back at the border. In fact, anyone whose ID identifies him or her as a member of any non-NAN military organization is denied admission to the nation. Relations with the UCAS became tense in

2045 when Washington requested permission to carry out war games on Sioux soil. The Sioux government rejected the request out-of-hand and stuck with their decision even after Washington made it clear that this was not an acceptable response. For two weeks the entire Sioux military machine hovered just short of total war-readiness status. It is not clear even now what would have happened if Washington had not backed down.

>>>>>[Ya know, I heard Washington pushed the buttons just to see how, and with what, the Sioux would respond. It's a trick reminiscent of the old cold war tactics between the old USA and Sov Union.]<<<<<
—Klink (12:19:42/10-28-52)

Though formidable when compared to other NAN nations, Sioux's armed forces are both outmanned and outgunned by UCAS forces. The Sioux government is painfully aware of this and is organized to operate on an undercover, partisan-style system should the nation be invaded. The Sioux nation is rumored to have a small supply of nuclear warheads, presumably purchased from one of several European powers, but it is believed that they have no delivery systems.

>>>>>[The real hard men are the Sioux Special Forces, nick-named the "Wildcats." These guys have borrowed tactics from the SEALS, the Green Berets, and even the Viet Cong, and they are basically unbeatable. They're always loaded for bear, and I get the feeling they're just looking for an opportunity to geek some-one—anyone. Not many are cybered, but I hear that most of the high-ranking officers have some wiz headware, including comlinks, on-board memory (mostly dedicated to tactical analysis data and algorithms), and so on. Danchekker didn't mention the incident in 2043, when UCAS started building a "prototype" wash-phase-array radar installation near the Sioux border. The UCAS said it was merely experimental, but the Sioux didn't like the fact that the installation had "firetrack" capabilities: in other words, it was designed to give precise terminal guidance to various nasty forms of munitions. It could also track rounds lobbed in its direction and coordinate immediate counterbattery fire before the first egg landed. It seems that two weeks before the site was scheduled to become operational, it blew up. An accident, everyone said, such an unfortunate accident. My sources say somebody "acciden-tally" planted several kilos of plastique in some strategic locations and "accidentally" detonated it. The operation has Wildcats written all over it.]<<<<<
—Hangfire (04:59:35/8-15-52)

>>>>>[I'm not too up on the mil-speak, Hangfire, but you've reminded me of another interesting item. The Wildcats and a few other units have resurrected the tradition of "honor feathers." Courageous acts are rewarded by the right to wear feathers identifying the deeds. Similar to medals, the feathers are a source of real pride to the recipients. Some civilians emulate the custom, particularly gang members, but god help them if a Wildcat catches them wearing real honor feathers they didn't earn…]<<<<<
—Holly (18:08:03/9-1-52)

FACTS AT A GLANCE

Population: 11,895,000

Human:	65%
Elf:	15%
Dwarf:	5%
Ork:	13%
Troll:	2%
Other:	0%

Per Capita Income: 33,000¥
Below Poverty Level: 11%
On Fortune's Active Traders List: 2%
Corporate Affiliation: 58%
Education:
High School Equivalency: 33%
College Equivalency: 42%
Advanced Studies Certificates: 15%
Regional Telecom Grid Access Code: NA/NAN/PCC

CLIMATE

The Pueblo nation is blessed with pleasant weather year-round. The area enjoys four distinct seasons, and each one is tourist season. During the summer, temperatures often exceed 30 degrees Celsius, but the humidity is so low that the heat is rarely uncomfortable. In the winter, the temperature drops well below zero and snow is common, particularly at high elevations. Again, however, low humidity mitigates much of the discomfort. Spring and fall are the recommended visiting times for elderly tourists and those suffering from cardio-pulmonary complaints.

ACCESS

Plane

Santa Fe, capital of the Pueblo nation, boasts one of the most modern and efficient international airports in North America, and perhaps the world. Suborbital and semiballistic flights connect to airports throughout the world on regular and dependable schedules. Slightly less regular are Vega flights to the various Skyport orbital stations in cis-terran space. These flights are usually restricted to those carrying governmental "undeniable requirement" authorization.

The Pueblo Council is justifiably proud of its "Airlink" transit system, a network of small, auto-piloted aircraft. Airlink pads are conveniently located in and around virtually every population center and offer a swift and efficient way of traveling around the nation. For those with private tilt-wing licenses, U-Push-It Inc. rents direct-piloted vehicles ranging from single-seat Hummingbirds to Federated Boeing Commuters to Osprey-class machines.

>>>>>[I'm blown away by the efficiency of the Airlink system. Even in rush-hour downtown Sante Fe, the maximum time I've ever waited for a medium-haul Airlink flight is 10 minutes. And their safety record is outstanding.]<<<<<
—Miyagi (16:14:49/2-10-52)

>>>>>[In general, I agree. But the system has problems with fliers that don't carry transponders. Airlink hushed it up really well, but last year one of their short-hop birds ran right into a wizworm who wasn't paying attention to right-of-way. Final score: two dead passengers and one pissed-off dragon.]<<<<<
—Toad (00:02:08/3-1-52)

Automobile or Bus

Major surface routes in the Pueblo nation include Highway 6 southwest from the Sioux nation, Highway 25 directly south from the Ute nation, Highway 160 east from California Free State via Ute, and Highways 550, 285, and 25 north from Aztlan. Whippet Bus Lines, Screaming Eagle Overland, and Steve's Buses run regular service into Colorado Springs from Omaha, Kansas City, Albuquerque, Salt Lake City, and Las Vegas.

>>>>>[Steve's Buses?!]<<<<<
—Donny J (16:19:30/4-19-52)

>>>>>[They've got a better on-time record than the other two, and they're cheaper. Believe it.]<<<<<
—Holly (11:07:31/4-20-52)

>>>>>[A note on good old Highway 160. As soon as it crosses the border into Ute, it becomes Route 666, the Highway of the Beast (see my entry under Ute).]<<<<<
—Bung (05:01:53/8-4-52)

TRIBAL DEMOGRAPHICS

The major tribes in the Pueblo nation are the Zuñi and Hopi. Each tribe accounts for almost half the nation, with other ethnic groups making up less than 3 percent of the total population. The government is almost perfectly balanced between the two tribes.

Humans are by far the majority, though the Pueblo nation treats metahumans more fairly than most other tribal nations. No sanctioned racial bias exists in government or in society as a whole.

>>>>>[Danchekker, chummer, if you believe that drek, I know a couple of bars you should check out.]<<<<<
— Big Bopper (09:31:59/3-1-52)

>>>>>[If you're talking about The Lariat, keep in mind that the owner used to be with the Humanis Policlub.]<<<<<
— Dude (20:16:33/3-1-52)

>>>>>[An interesting dichotomy can be seen between the two major tribes. The Zuñi are generally quiet, conservative people who live a structured life. They avoid extremes of emotion in public. The Hopi, on the other hand, seem to be more dissatisfied about things in general. If you see a demonstration in the Pueblo nation, most of the protesters are going to be Hopi. The majority of Pueblo shadowrunners—and, interestingly enough, the majority of cops—are Hopi.]<<<<<
— Holly (13:14:47/4-9-52)

>>>>>[We Hopi have a saying: "One Hopi makes a good friend. Two Hopi makes a disagreement. Three Hopi makes a headache."]<<<<<
— Nevada (20:39:19/4-13-52)

>>>>>[Pueblo has its share of "back-to-the-landers," people who embrace as many of the old traditions as they can and still be comfortable. (Most don't give up their air conditioners, for example.) These people wear their hair in a distinctive fashion, trimmed to just above the eyebrows and ears and long in the back. The men often wear silver and turquoise jewelry.]<<<<<
— People Watcher (21:23:56/8-14-52)

The Pueblo nation has very few residents of non-Amerindian extraction. Unlike other NAN nations, Pueblo abided by the letter of the Treaty of Denver, rather than the spirit, and expelled all non-native people from its lands. The government eventually recognized the problems inherent in this attitude. Denying a prospective immigrant entry into the nation simply because he or she was non-native would eventually prove detrimental to technological advancement. The number of non-natives is still no more than 5 percent of the population, however, and the majority are a part of the business community in one way or another.

>>>>>[We have our own tribe, but it sure as drek ain't official. We're the Underground Awakened: orks and trolls, even some dwarfs. We have our own homeland, too, under Pueblo, but I'm not about to tell you just where. We have our own tribal council, tribal elders, and all that drek. We can't live in the old ways, time and our bodies have seen to that. But we *can* keep what's good from our heritage. We're living the old traditions, and if you'd like to try and stop us, you'll find we're the meanest motherfragging tribe you've ever seen.]<<<<<
— Hulk (23:29:38/3-29-52)

HISTORY AND CULTURE

Historically, the Southwest region boasted a cultural diversity greater than any other region in North America. The Anasazi built cliff houses in the northern area of the region. The Hohokam dug long irrigation canals in what became central Arizona. The Mogollon hunted and farmed along the rivers of eastern Arizona and western New Mexico. The Pueblo tribes, the Acoma, Hopi, Laguna, San Ildefonso, Taos, Zia, and Zuñi, descended from the early Anasazi Indians and had one of the most highly developed civilizations on the continent. The Pueblo tribes lived in villages and farmed along rivers that provided enough water to irrigate their crops. The Papago, Pima, and Yuma also farmed, though hunting and gathering provided much of their food. They lived in villages, moving when the seasons changed and living a simpler life than the Pueblo tribes.

Other tribes in the region often raided the peaceful Pueblo peoples. The invaders included warlike tribes such as the Apache and Navaho, who were related to the Athabaskan-speaking tribes of northwest Canada.

In 1540, a Spanish explorer, Francisco de Coronado, was the first European to meet the Amerindians of this region. As in the California-Intermountain region, the Spanish set up missions and tried to convert the natives to Christianity. Unfortunately, this attempted conversion included the proscription of all native religious ceremonies. The Amerindians refused to abandon their traditions, leading to strife between the natives and Europeans. Led by Popé, the Pueblo revolted in 1680. The rebellion lasted until 1700. Rather than suffer the painfully re-established yoke of the Europeans, many Pueblos fled to the Navaho tribes, who were outside the area most tightly controlled by the Spaniards. This move led to significant cultural cross-pollination. The Navaho learned many skills from the Pueblo, including cloth weaving, fruit-farming, and sheep herding, and also adopted many Pueblo religious practices.

>>>>[So this is how the Great Ghost Dance got spread around.]<<<<<
— Camille (18:29:58/6-30-52)

>>>>>[The first time.]<<<<<
— Holly (06:18:23/7-2-52)

In later encounters with the Europeans, especially land struggles, the tribes of the Southwest region offered less armed resistance than did other tribes. Their relocation to reservations was accomplished with very little bloodshed and was complete by the middle of the 20th century. In the years following, many tribes suffered cultural evaporation, their younger members abandoning the traditions of their forefathers to integrate with non-native society. By the beginning of the Year of Chaos, the only two tribes with any significant presence in the area were the Zuñi and the Hopi.

In the conflict between Amerindians and non-natives, neither the Zuni nor the Hopi participated in the fighting, at least not in regular military actions.

>>>>>[Not true. Bands of Hopi joined in the armed struggle.]<<<<<
— Bast (14:44:19/3-29-52)

>>>>>[…and honored themselves in the fighting. But they were rare. Most Zuñi and Hopi—particularly the former—dedicated their efforts to the struggle in a different way. See Danchekker's next comments.]<<<<<
—People Watcher (09:54:59/4-19-52)

The Spaniards tried to suppress the traditional Pueblo religious rituals. When the Southwest became a part of the United States, however, the Amerindians were once again free to celebrate their religion openly. Their rituals became particularly significant when magic returned to the world. Many traditional Amerindian rituals probably originated in earlier times when magic was a way of life. Many of these rituals changed almost beyond recognition, however, for even the strongest-held tradition mutates with time.

>>>>>[But when was this "earlier time when magic was a way of life"? We know there was no magic during the peak of the Amerindian culture in North America. It is a matter of historical record. Does it go further back, to before their emigration across the Bering Strait? Does anyone know? Can anyone guess?]<<<<<
—Jake (13:09:14/5-17-52)

>>>>>[Oh, I'm sure someone knows. But will they say? I don't think so.]<<<<<
—Flute (21:31:14/5-19-52)

When the mana reached a certain level, the Pueblo rituals again summoned power, as they had many years before. The Pueblo shamans now had an edge over shamans from other cultures who had lost or forsaken their traditional religions. The Pueblo tribes sent many members and much power to the Great Ghost Dance, and many shamanic "active response teams" aided the guerrilla war.

>>>>>[That's a part of the war we don't hear much about. One of my buddies was a "field shaman" with a strike team, and the stories he told would curl your hair. But I guess those who fought in the war want to keep their tricks of the trade secret, just in case they need them again. (Are you listening, Anglos?)]<<<<<
—Taos (20:35:17/3-11-52)

The Pueblo tribes maintained their religious and magical traditions. They did not turn their backs on the advantages of technology, however. Except for the Makah, the Zuñi and Hopi tribes have been highly receptive to scientific advancement. While shamans refined the practice of magic, Pueblo "technomancers" bent to their wills the complexities of the microchip and genetic intron. The Pueblo nation strikes an even, efficient balance between tradition and technology.

>>>>>[…a balance I wish other native nations could achieve. In balance lies strength.]<<<<<
—Man-of-Many-Names (17:08:57/8-30-52)

The Pueblo nation today is a fascinating blend of the old and the new. On the streets, businessmen dressed in the latest corporate fashions rub shoulders with others wearing woven cotton kilts. Keeping ancient handicrafts, such as pottery and woven blanket work, alive is very important to the Pueblos. Unlike the governments of other nations, the Pueblo Corporate Council does not actively market its artwork outside the country.

>>>>>[Which tells you this isn't the kind of "genuine simulated Injun art" that the Cascade Orks (and certain other tribes) peddle. This is art for art's sake, to preserve the knowledge of cherished traditions.]<<<<<
—Holly (19:04:20/3-09-52)

>>>>>[Oh, yes, pretty Holly. It just gets me right *here*.]<<<<<
—Cascade Trog (18:09:23/4-25-52)

>>>>>[There's another wizzer tradition they're not keen to lose, and this one's a lot more important to you runners out there than a blanket or clay rattle. The Hopi used these boomerang-like throwing sticks to hunt game a long time ago. Well, they haven't forgotten how to use them—or else they've resurrected the technique. Most Hopi own at least one of these, and take great pride and honor in achieving pinpoint accuracy in their use. (And believe me, some people have achieved unbelievable accuracy.)]<<<<<
—Sapper (21:16:31/7-10-52)

A TRIBE IN PERSPECTIVE: THE ZUÑI

Though this tribe is referred to as the Zuñi by catalogers and anthropologists, members of this tribe almost always refer to themselves as Ashiwi (pronounced AH shee wee, "the people" in the Penutian language). In this discussion, we use the common name.

The Zuñi once lived in seven pueblo villages situated around Gallup, New Mexico. The Spanish explorers called these villages "The Seven Cities of Cibola." The tribe eventually abandoned all these towns but one, Zuñi, which was south of Gallup. By the middle to late 20th century, the Zuñi abandoned their terraced buildings altogether and constructed individual one-story houses of purplish sandstone.

The Zuñi suffered significant cultural evaporation during this same period. It affected Zuñi culture, but not as severely as other groups, including the Hopi, for a fascinating reason. The Zuñi men had an unmatched reputation as firefighters. Every summer, the Zuñi traveled to fight forest fires throughout the West. Even more than their traditional dances and ceremonies, their firefighting served as a cultural anchor for the tribe and held it together.

As did the Hopi, the Zuñi clung to their traditional religious ceremonies and rituals. The firefighting disrupted their ceremonial calendar during the summer, but every fall the tribe performed the colorful Shalako ceremony. When the Zuñi realized that their ceremonies were summoning the ancient powers again, they examined their religious calendar in order to take full advantage of the newly reawakened magic. Research quickly showed the shamans that their ceremonial calendar had grown inaccurate over the years, so they shifted to a sidereal calendar that realigned their ceremonies with the natural rhythms of magic.

The reappearance of magic and the recognition that the old traditions were more than mumbo-jumbo halted and even reversed the cultural evaporation the tribe had been suffering. Young adults returned to the tribe, bringing with them an appreciation for and understanding of modern technology. The tribe embraced these new developments and began to find effective uses for them.

When the struggles between the Amerindian nations and the United States government heated up, the Zuñi used their powerful weather-based magics from behind the lines to disrupt enemy supply lines and troop movements. They also provided tactical and logistic support to Hopi strike teams.

>>>>>[Don't think that the Zuñi were less committed to the struggle than were the Hopi. They simply knew where their strengths lay and used them to their best advantage. A peaceable people, they didn't find it as easy as the Hopi to turn aside from their tradition of nonviolence. They put a lot of effort into messing things up from afar, however, kind of like magical artillery, and they became technology brokers for many of the southwestern tribes. (That is, they cut deals with the Japanese and others to access some real wiz tech, then supplied it to other tribes along with instruction on its use.)]<<<<<
—People Watcher (16:13:17/11-25-52)

>>>>>[This violence/non-violence issue isn't as cut and dried as it might sound. Not all Hopi agreed that violence was the way to go, and not all Zuñi were pacifists. And a significant proportion of both tribes abhors killing. If they kill someone in war or in a police action, only several days of purification and atonement will make them feel worthy to rejoin their community.]<<<<<
—Holly (15:50:58/11-28-52)

The Zuñi have gone beyond even the Hopi in maintaining traditional artistic skills. Jewelry-making is one of the main traditional art forms still practiced, using silver combined with turquoise, shell, and jet.

>>>>>[Interesting, huh? The major exports of the PCC are silverwork and software.]<<<<<
—The Keynesian Kid (00:04:18/6-13-52)

The Zuñi have resurrected a traditional ceremony called kachina worship. The Kachina Society is a group of masked dancers, all male, who perform rain ceremonies to ensure good crops. Their traditional ceremonial garb is a white kilt or wraparound skirt with red ribbons or bands on the left hip. The upper body is left bare except for a necklace of shell, stone, or silver, and a red sash running from the right shoulder to the left hip. The masks exaggerate beards, eyebrows, and noses. Eagle or hawk feathers are usually attached to the back of the dancer's head. The Kachinas chant and dance to the rhythm of rattles. Interestingly enough, few of the Kachina dancers are shamans, and their rituals and ceremonies generally lack any real power.

>>>>>[Not always true. Some subgroups within the Kachina Society are exclusively shamanic and their ceremonies are powerful enough to make your fragging hair stand on end. The Kachinas reappeared during the war between NAN and the US government. Some anthropologists, myself included, believe it was camouflage to make it more difficult for deep penetration agents to assassinate top shamans. If you can't tell one Kachina from another—a dancer with real power from a dancer with none—within a group all wearing masks, it becomes tougher to carry out an organized campaign of assassination. Of course, that theory doesn't explain why the Kachinas are still around. The members of the Kachina Society decline to confirm or deny this theory. (Understandably, I guess.)]<<<<<
—People Watcher (16:00:48/7-8-52)

>>>>>[I'm not sure I agree fully with People Watcher and his faction, but it's as good a theory as any and it's reinforced by the fact that the Kachinas won't discuss the reappearance of the Society. One more interesting fact about the dancers that People Watcher doesn't mention is that the Kachina Society is a Hopi, *not* a Zuñi, tradition. The Zuñi shamans may have chosen kachina worship as a convenient tradition to protect them during the war, or this may be another example of the cultural and traditional drift that occurs with time. It's really a coin toss.]<<<<<
—Holly (15:48:37/7-11-52)

▼ ▼ ▼ ▼ ▼ ▼

ECONOMY

Unlike the majority of Amerindian nations, the Pueblo Corporate Council is not dependent on either primary (resource-based) or secondary (manufacturing) industry for its prosperity. Instead, the country bases its economy on a strong tertiary industry, information processing. Many breakthroughs in software development methodology and computer hardware design have come out of Pueblo's small high-technology corporations.

>>>>>[Small is a relative word here. If you exclude diversified companies and international conglomerates, three of the world's five largest software developers are Pueblo-based: Tablelands, Iris, and Virtual Reality. (This ranking is based on annual sales.)]<<<<<
—Nand (01:34:48/8-20-52)

>>>>>[And don't forget the Corporate Council itself: it's got a team of drek-hot deckers and analysts on staff. A lot of their work never sees the light of day, it just gets incorporated into the Council's central computer network. But they do commercialize the occasional piece of software. (You know "Pigeonhole," the freeform multi-relational database? That's a Pueblo product.) And just because it's not officially released doesn't mean a particular development doesn't leave Pueblo. I hear from unimpeachable sources that Renraku's new black IC, the stuff that geeked one of the Darkside Deckers last month, was actually stolen from Pueblo.]<<<<<
—FastJack (15:53:18/8-20-52)

>>>>>[Yeah, by you.]<<<<<
—Darkside (17:34:58/9-01-52)

The Pueblo nation is the most prosperous country in North America. They boast the highest standard of living, and the government offers the widest range of social services of any nation. The nation produces very little of its own food. Even taking into account the importation of almost all foodstuffs, however, the nation's trade balance is the envy of all North America.

The vast majority of business in the Pueblo nation is conducted by Pueblo-based corporations. The major multinationals and conglomerates have only a small presence. Any non-Pueblo-based corporation with an annual income of over 100 million nuyen must apply for a license to do business in the Pueblo nation. Such companies' operations are reviewed annually according to stringent "fair practices" laws, and their license may be revoked if these laws are broken.

>>>>>[These laws are not anti-competitive, nor do they give Pueblo-based companies any advantage. They do make strictly illegal many of the strong-arm tactics that the big corps use freely everywhere else in the world.]<<<<<
—Unsuit (01:51:55/3-10-52)

>>>>[The council's regulatory body really knows its drek, chummer. They check into every applicant company's ownership, and they know every trick in the fragging book: shell companies, indirect ownership, strawmen, the works. And even if things look cool on the surface, they've got real smooth deckers who can crack into anything to make sure it's cool under the surface too.]<<<<<
—Digital Alien (03:50:26/3-18-52)

>>>>>[I don't know the details, but the Big A is on "show-cause" for something. If they cross the line again they get their license pulled, and it's goodbye Charlie.]<<<<<
—Pyramid Watcher (23:00:14/5-7-52)

As its name implies, the Pueblo Corporate Council is organized as a corporation. Citizens of the nation are actually shareholders in the corporation. Citizenship automatically assigns the individual one share in the corporation. Citizens are free to buy further shares either directly from the government or on the secondary market. It is, however, strictly illegal for a citizen to sell his or her last corporate share without first relinquishing Pueblo citizenship. If the corporation shows a profit at the end of the fiscal year, profit is returned to the shareholders in the form of dividends, which can be taken in cash or applied to mitigate the individual citizen's tax burden. Even after the corporation has farmed most of its profits back into the nation to maintain the infrastructure and so on, the nation is issuing a dividend not less than 3 percent of a corporate share's current value. In addition, the shares have shown significant capital growth. Taking all factors into account, Pueblo Corporate Council shares have posted a five-year average Return On Investment of 9.2 percent.

>>>>>[When you consider that Aztechnology posted a five-year average ROI of under 4 percent, that's fragging good.]<<<<<
—Maynard (10:41:41/4-1-52)

>>>>>[And what's the current interest rate paid by banks: around 4 percent and change? It's one hell of a good investment. Too bad only Pueblo citizens can buy into the corporation.]<<<<<
—Turtle (20:49:54/4-3-52)

>>>>>[…officially, that is.]<<<<<
—Maynard (15:19:20/4-4-52)

>>>>>[The current on-line quotation lists Pueblo shares at 7,389¥ each, an all-time high.]<<<<<
—Bellingham Broker (05:42:50/11-23-52)

>>>>>[Cost differential time again. Baseline is Seattle.

PUEBLO COST OF LIVING

ITEM	COST
Weaponry	
Ammunition	90% (1)
Explosives	— (3)
Firearm Accessories	90% (2)
Firearms	90%
Melee Weapons	100%
Projectile Weapons	100%
Throwing Weapons	95%
Armor	
Armor	100% (4)
Security and Surveillance	
Communications	80%
Security Devices	80%
Surveillance Countermeasures	90%
Surveillance Measures	90%
Survival Gear	100%
Vision Enhancers	80%
Lifestyle	
Lifestyle	95%
Electronics	
Electronics	80%
Cybertech	
Biotech	100%
Bodyware	100%
Cyberdecks	90% (5)
Headware	90%
Internals	90%
Programs	85%
Magical Equipment	
Hermetic Library	130%
Magical Supplies	110%
Magical Weapons	120%
Power Foci	100%
Ritual Sorcery Materials	110%
Spell Foci	100%
Vehicles	
Aircraft	100%
Boats	110%
Ground Vehicles	80%
Military Vehicles	— (6)

Cost of Living—Notes:

(1) As you'd expect, the real wizzer stuff is restricted. And in Pueblo, "restricted" is "RESTRICTED" in big, quivering capital letters.

(2) Recoil compensation is kosher, since you might want it for your hunting weapons. Silencers, smartlinks, and so on are restricted.

(3) You'll probably find this as hard to believe as I did, but the government's ban on non-licensed possession of explosives is actually *working!* This stuff is tough to lay hands on, and prices are whatever the market will bear.

(4) Light body armor only: everything else is so restricted that even the major corp security forces aren't allowed to have it (officially).

(5) Virtual Reality Inc. markets a real wiz product. Of course, being the law-abiding souls that they are, the deck inserts an official identcode into the matrix wherever you deck in. Luckily, freelance electron pushers are available to remove that little embarrassment from the deck…for a fee.

(6) Think about it. If the Corp Council doesn't like you having body armor, are they going to be jazzed if you've got a tank?

Tech is cheap, and it's fragging good quality. You don't need a t-bird run to transport software or small high-tech goodies, but there's definitely a healthy smuggling business out of Pueblo into the neighboring nations. And *definitely* check the section on Denver.]<<<<<
—The Keynesian Kid (19:02:47/2-11-52)

>>>>>[The Kid doesn't mention it, but one area where the Pueblo is very much into manufacturing as well as design is security-grade and military weapons/ordnance. The Pueblo Security Force, which serves as both cops and army, is probably the best-equipped force in NA, and their stuff is all local manufacture. (Granted, a lot of it's under license from Ares and Colt, among others, but manufacture and assembly all take place in Pueblo.)]<<<<<
—Toshikazu (07:10:47/6-10-52)

>>>>>[Even on Ares-designed hardware, the failure rate is significantly lower on Pueblo-built models. The same goes for heavy armor.]<<<<<
—Hangfire (23:20:41/6-14-52)

GOVERNMENT

The supreme governing body in the Pueblo Corporate Council is the Board of Directors. The twelve board members are selected by general election in which all shareholders (i.e., citizens) of the corporation are entitled to vote. Individuals' votes are weighted according to the number of corporate shares they hold, but this weighting is not a linear relationship. Instead, the weighting applied is log to the base 10 of the number of shares held, plus one. In other words, a citizen with one share has a weighting of 1 (log of 1 equals 0, plus 1), while a citizen holding one million shares has a weighting of 7 (log of 1,000,000 equals 6, plus 1).

>>>>>[Typical plutocratic mentality. The power is held by those who have the wealth. Nothing new there, it's just out in the open for once. It makes me sick.]<<<<<
    —Peter (17:40:24/3-2-52)

>>>>>[Hold on there, chummer. The fact that it *is* out in the open makes a *big* difference. I don't see anything innately wrong with this system.]<<<<<
    —The Keynesian Kid (13:29:50/3-9-52)

>>>>>[You don't, you drek-nosed slot? Doesn't it bother you that—well, let's use Danchekker's example. Doesn't it bother you that the opinion of a citizen holding one million shares is worth seven times the opinion of the poor sod on the street who only holds one share? What about one man, one vote?]<<<<<
    —Peter (23:58:29/3-9-52)

>>>>>[First off, chummer, let's keep the emotional rhetoric and insults out of it. Okay. One share in the corporation costs something like 7,000¥, right? Taking your example, a guy who's kicked close to 7 billion nuyen into the running of the government has seven times the say of the chummer who hasn't put in one red cent. That means that eight squatters can out-vote your multi-billionaire. Doesn't sound too disruptive to me, chummer, and the ethics of it don't choke me either. If I put 7 billion nuyen into something, I think I'd like an increased say, even an indirect one, about how my money's being used.]<<<<<
    —The Keynesian Kid (00:38:14/3-10-52)

>>>>>[Gravy-sucking capitalist running dog.]<<<<<
    —Peter (00:41:07/3-10-52)

>>>>>[Smile when you say that, chummer…]<<<<<
    —The Keynesian Kid (00:41:50/3-10-52)

>>>>>[Open advice to Peter: Don't get the Kid riled, it just isn't healthy. Ever seen a chromed accountant with an attitude? Not a pretty sight…]<<<<<
    —Cyn (00:42:51/3-10-52)

>>>>>[Love you too, Cyn.]<<<<<
    —The Keynesian Kid (00:43:29/3-10-52)

The board must be consulted on all matters of international policy and must approve any decision to spend more than 25 billion nuyen of corporate funds. It is also responsible for selecting the president and vice-presidents of the corporation.

The day-to-day administration of the corporation is in the hands of the Executive Committee, the president and vice-presidents. Tenure in these positions is determined by the board. Executives who show the slightest hint of incompetence or corruption are quickly purged. The executive committee is responsible for the ongoing operation of the corporation, and setting internal policy. The Board has discretionary veto power over any decision of the executive council, though they have never used it. Executive Committee members' salaries are commensurate with equivalent positions in major multinationals.

>>>>>[Translation: The prez pulls down damn near a mil annually.]<<<<<
    —Nuyen Nick (07:08:25/2-18-52)

>>>>>[Sounds like a lot, huh? But think about it. The majority of elected officials in other countries are ex-used car salesmen, ex-hardware-store owners, ex-actors, ad fragging nauseam. And a lot of them are power-hungry no-minds. Why can't government attract really competent types? One reason is compensation: Why should the CEO of a major corporation put up with all the drek that politicos face and take a cut in pay? At least in Pueblo it's financially worthwhile for a top-notch manager to consider a career in politics.]<<<<<
    —Skeleton Hunter (10:26:22/2-23-52)

>>>>>[Well said, Hunter. By comparison, the board members take home a salary officially fixed at 1¥ per year. Interesting, eh?]<<<<<
    —Scavenger (00:06:03/2-28-52)

>>>>>[The Chairman of the Board is Carlos Estefan, a Dog shaman and about three years older than god. The president is Maria Alonzo. A mundane (I think), no obvious chrome, but able to persuade a shark feeding-frenzy to line up politely and take turns.]<<<<<
    —Sol (08:46:53/4-9-52)

LAWS

IMMIGRATION

The Pueblo nation has the highest population density of any North American country. It is the only NAN nation not suffering from a depleted population. In general, the nation is free to be very selective when it comes to accepting immigrants. The selection procedure is impartial with regard to race and sex, but holds stringent standards for skills and education level. (This also means that a candidate who qualifies for immigration on the basis of education and training is rarely penalized for non-tribal heritage.) Every three months, the Department of Immigration compiles a list of skills and job classifications in national demand. Prospective immigrants who fit these classifications are allowed to become citizens. Prospective immigrants who do not match the "hot list" can only become a citizen by sponsorship from a Pueblo-based corporation. The sponsoring corporation must agree to employ the immigrant for a minimum of 12 months and must prove that the position could not be adequately filled by a Pueblo citizen. Work visas are not available. Non-citizens are simply not allowed to work within the Pueblo nation. Visitors and tourists are welcome.

>>>>>[Sponsorship isn't the rubber-stamp matter it is in Algonkian-Manitoo. If a company needs a skill set that can't be found in Pueblo, you can bet your last nuyen that that skill set is going to be on the next hot list.]<<<<<
—Captain Chaos (00:31:08/3-30-52)

On becoming a citizen of the Pueblo Corporate Council, an immigrant must permanently relinquish any other citizenships currently held. In addition, the immigrant must purchase at least one share in the corporation at the current market price. If a citizen relinquishes Pueblo citizenship, he or she must sell all currently held shares back to the corporation at the market price. The Corporation does not charge brokerage fees for either of these transactions.

CIVIL AND TRIBAL LAWS

The Pueblo justice system is based on a system of shamanic tribunals. Each region has one or more tribunals, a number based on the region's population. A tribunal comprises three shamans who are selected by the Department of Justice (under the guidance of the Vice-President, Justice) plus support staff. Suspects in criminal matters are bound over to the appropriate tribunal by the Security Force until the tribunal schedules a trial date. In the case of civil matters, litigation, and so on, the plaintiff is responsible for approaching the tribunal and showing sufficient cause to schedule a court date.

The trial has a structure similar to a UCAS court-martial. Prosecutors and defense attorneys appear for their clients, but the shamanic judges participate more in the investigatory phases than UCAS civil judges. The shamanic judges often exercise their right to use magic to authenticate the evidence and testimony brought before them.

>>>>>[Frag, don't ever, ever, ever try to suborn a shamanic judge. These guys are just too straight-arrow to be real, and they don't accept the traditional defense of "Just kidding!" And if you don't believe me, ask Shirell Roseman—he's doing five to ten in Sante Fe for trying to improve a judge's cash flow.]<<<<<
—Bung (00:13:50/1-17-90)

>>>>>[Computer crime and weapons offenses are big no-nos in Pueblo. These laws are strictly enforced and the penalties imposed, whether fines or hard time, are typically around 150 percent of what you'd pick up in Seattle.]<<<<<
—Legal Beagle (19:50:18/7-22-52)

>>>>>[Enforcement is in the hands of the Pueblo Security Force, and what a bunch of hard-line boyos we're talking here. A SecForce trooper serves equal time in the Civilian Arm (police) and the Defense Arm (national armed forces) and the cross-training shows. The cops are as well-trained as Desert Wars veterans (in fact, some cops *are* Desert Wars veterans) and pack military-grade hardware when the situation demands. Normally they carry machine pistols and wear light armored jackets, but if things get hairy they go to heavy armor and anything from assault shotguns to gyro-mount cannon or even pulse-laser units. They've got plenty of surface and air support, and their command and control set-up would give a lot of UCAS generals wet dreams. And remember, because the Civilian and Defense Arms are really the same outfit, the cops can mobilize a full military response with a single call.]<<<<<
     —Hatchetman (23:59:21/7-24-52)

>>>>>[Cyber?]<<<<<
     —Rat (00:01:24/7-25-52)

>>>>>[Some are chromed, a few to the max, and many have some type of headware. Scary stuff, chummer, so don't slot with these guys. If they need it, they've got the hardware to guarantee a one-shot take-down on anything. *Anything.*]<<<<<
     —Hatchetman (00:03:52/7-25-52)

>>>>>[Remember, the majority of the SecForce is Hopi—the more dissatisfied segment of the population. Get my drift?]<<<<<
     —Holly (01:35:08/10-11-52

>>>>>[Lately it's been said that the Sioux have not been as forceful as they could be about interdicting the BTL trade leaking into the Pueblo Council. The Sioux, of course, claim they are doing everything they can, but...]<<<<<
     —Wacko (21:10:47/10-11-52)

>>>>>[Here's another look at defense. Chummers, you may think you've seen sophisticated computer systems. Aztechnology and Renraku in Seattle, Hyundai-IBM in Armonk, or the Alliance Franáaise in Québec—but you ain't seen nothing till you've tried to deck the Pueblo corporate system. It's part of the Matrix, but the level of sophistication is literally years ahead of any other part of the net. And, chummer, you might think you can cut any ice, but I'd be willing to bet anything you can't cut theirs. (Even trying, you'd be betting your life.) Reactive black ice, AI-run constructs, trace-and-burn, logic mines, watchdogs, trackers—these guys know it all. Frag, they consult out to other big corps who want deadly systems, and it's chip-truth they wouldn't give away their best secrets. If that isn't bad enough, the corp has the Pueblo's best deckers on staff. (It's a great deal for the deckers: they get to play with the absolute cutting edge of hardware, and can work the bugs out of their most perverted and cruel software *legally*.) If anybody managed to cut the ice, he'd have a handful of drek-hot deckers on his butt before you could say slot and run. The decker brigade is officially a part of the Security Force (both Civil and Defense), which means they cooperate nice and tight with the cops on the street. The deckers can trace and dump you and the cops will be there to pick you up before your head stops spinning. Fragging charming.]<<<<<
     —Core Warrior (09:32:58/10-12-52)

>>>>>[The ice is so bad that FastJack got himself geeked trying to crack Pueblo.]<<<<<
     —Anonymous (03:42:31/10-15-52)

>>>>>[Reports of my geeking have been greatly exaggerated. The ice *is* serious drek, though.]<<<<<
     —FastJack (10:59:25/10-19-52)

>>>>>[I keep hearing rumors that the Pueblo network has "woken up." The reasoning runs like this: The only real difference between a (meta)human brain and a computer system is the number of "neural" connections. Once the number of connections exceeds a certain limit, intelligence, and, hypothetically, self-awareness, though possibly self-awareness of a totally alien nature, *must* develop. The version I keep hearing is that the guys at Pueblo have linked everything they've got into a tightly integrated subnet within the Matrix...and that subnet has passed the basic limit. Could very well be drek, probably is...but intelligence would explain Core Warrior's "AI-run constructs," right? They could be consciously controlled "antibodies." How would such an intelligence view (meta)humans—and particularly deckers?]<<<<<
     —Turing II (22:42:44/10-24-52)

>>>>>[I hear the same rumors. Discounting the intelligence aspect, which I can't prove or disprove, there's still an interesting point to be made. If Pueblo linked "everything they've got" into their own subnet, then when you crash the subnet, you crash Pueblo. (Foolish for Pueblo, tempting for me.) According to power dynamics theory, any power network, whether your Harley's engine or the Pueblo net, has at least one "choke point" where all the power is concentrated. Crash that chokepoint, the system goes down. (Your engine can be running fine, but if I cut your chain you go nowhere.) I analyzed the Pueblo subnet. Result: no choke point. Conclusion: either power dynamics theory is wrong, or I haven't dug deeply enough. More anon.]<<<<<
—Captain Chaos (14:13:42/11-15-52)

INTERNATIONAL RELATIONS

The Pueblo Corporate Council is on good terms with all its neighbors, with the notable exception of Aztlan. Diplomatic relations are definitely cool, though not hostile. Both countries use countervailing duties to make trading between them less attractive.

>>>>>[That makes a weird kind of sense if what they say about the tight links between the Aztlan government and Aztechnology is true. Pueblo won't waive its fair practices laws and is threatening to lift the Big A's license. The Aztlan government would have plenty of incentive to get into the act.]<<<<<
—Pyramid Watcher (10:44:42/7-23-52)

>>>>>[There's another reason for their concern. Pueblo was shaken up by the Aztlan-Texas War of 2035, and unconsidered political responses on both sides led to strained diplomatic relations between Pueblo and Aztlan. They've remained that way. Another consequence of the war is that Pueblo and CAS are pretty buddy-buddy lately.]<<<<<
—Dilly (02:03:50/7-26-52)

>>>>>["Buddy-buddy" is an understatement, Dilly. They've got their hands in each other's pockets and their noses up each other's...well, you get the idea. Both countries think that their informal deal to exchange military intelligence, mainly about Aztlan, is a secret, so don't tell. If one country digs up some info, it's passed to the other country. The military intelligence guys had a nice, smooth, secure channel set up to take care of the exchange, but then the politicos got involved. Politicians are as good for intelligence operations as napalm is for ice sculptures, so naturally the whole deal is now an open secret. Aztlan knows, that's for sure. (Leak info to Pueblo and watch the CAS politicos respond. *Sure* there's no collaboration.)]<<<<<
—Flashburn (23:56:13/8-13-52)

The Pueblo nation has one of the strongest voices on the NAN Sovereign Council. This is a function of the country's technological superiority and enviable balance of trade, not population.

>>>>>[A strong grass-roots movement proposes that Pueblo secede from the NAN. The Pueblos see their involvement with the other Amerind nations as a hindrance, because nothing positive comes from their association. This feeling is getting stronger now that the NAN is talking about "transfer payments" to aid the less financially secure nations. The people of Pueblo know which side of that equation they're going to be on. Pueblo's representative to the Sovereign Council is David Blacksilver, and he supports Pueblo's continued membership in the NAN...but you can bet he'll fight tooth and nail against the proposed transfer payments.]<<<<<
—Rick O'Shay (19:39:50/4-11-52)

>>>>>[David Blacksilver used to run the shadows under the name Artemis. The last few years he hasn't kept up with developments in the decker world, but I know he could still show the majority of runners a trick or two.]<<<<<
—Nand (07:11:54/4-13-52)

The Pueblo nation enjoys close diplomatic relations and trade ties with Japan and its proxy government in California Free State. MITI, the Japanese ministry responsible for coordinating technological growth, works hand-in-hand with the corresponding agency in the Pueblo government to put together deals advantageous to both parties. Several major joint-venture projects are in the works between Japanese and Pueblo corporations.

>>>>>[Iris is about to get into bed with Renraku. The grapevine says that the entire Iris executive echelon was shipped over to Renraku's HQ in Chiba and came back with their socks blown off. My guess is we'll be seeing Iris firmware together with Renraku hardware, but I don't know what the application's going to be. Be forewarned: it's going to be mega-hot.]<<<<<
—CP-You (00:18:53/1-29-52)

>>>>>[I'm surprised that Danchekker didn't emphasize this: despite Pueblo's high-tech corporate rep, it's still a very magically aware nation. Many of those in power are shamans, and those that aren't have shamans on their staff. And when I say "shamans" I mean SHAMANS, guys and gals with real power. The power isn't used openly, and not on a regular basis, but it's there behind the scenes to be wheeled out like a big gun. And another thing; I think the Pueblo boys are into serious weather magic.]<<<<<
—Coyote (14:20:30/5-24-52)

>>>>>[Coyote's right. It was mentioned in passing earlier, but it's worth stressing: the Great Ghost Dance is a Zuñi tradition. That's right, the Great Ghost Dance that Daniel Howling Coyote, a Ute, used to toast the army. I don't know if he knew the Dance before the NAN started getting together or if he learned it after. In any case, it's an indication of just how much traditions, as well as tribes and peoples, have mixed and assimilated. The Dance is all about weather magic, controlling the elements. Every year near midsummer, a group of Zuñi and Hopi shamans and their followers camp for five days and nights in the foothills of the Rockies. I don't know what they do there, because outsiders are not invited, but I *do* know that weather patterns go wild all through the area around the camp. Storms, high wind, lightning—it's quite a show.]<<<<<
—People Watcher (17:37:27/6-1-52)

DENVER

During the chaotic years between 2011, when Daniel Howling Coyote led his followers out of the Abilene Re-Education Camp, and the signing of the Treaty of Denver in 2018, Denver became a city beleaguered. Its significance as a communications and transportation hub was obvious to everyone, and the fledgling nations into which North America had split began maneuvering for possession of the city.

Four new nations, Aztlan, Pueblo, Sioux, and Ute, claimed it as part of their territory, backing up their claims with equally plausible historical rationalizations. The problem with all these claimants was that, before the signing of the Treaty, no other nation in the world officially recognized their sovereignty. How could a non-nation claim that a city was in its (non-existent) territory? Naturally, the United States wanted to keep control of the city and the pathways leading to it.

The Treaty of Denver settled the dispute, but in a rather unusual way. Instead of giving the city to only one claimant, the Treaty commission decided to order a compromise. A confederation of all five claimants would govern the city. The supreme governing body would be a Council made up of one representative from each of the five claimant nations, and all Council decisions would require agreement from three of the representatives. Denver became extraterritorial to all nations. No country could levy national taxes or trade tariffs on Denver. Denver residents would pay city taxes, an amount to be set by the Council, to cover government expenses and maintain the infrastructure. Furthermore, no nation would be allowed to station military forces in the city or move military personnel within the boundaries of the city, which now extended far beyond the original city limits.

>>>>>[Obviously, the Treaty Commission didn't understand the military mind. No country has military units in Denver, but they all have "civilian security services" which have engaged their corresponding armed forces as "consultants" and "advisors." Though the security forces are strictly civilian, they're armed with military-grade weapons and have undergone military training.]<<<<<
—Hangfire (20:06:55/3-5-52)

>>>>>[Watch out for the sec forces in the Sioux sector. They're anchored by a central cadre of "retired" Sioux Special Forces—that's right, chummers, Wildcats. And we all know the stories about them; shamanic commandos, armed to the teeth and trained to the max. Not a cool place to start trouble.]<<<<<
—Rex (15:30:26/3-10-52)

The Treaty of Denver specifically stated that the city would be "open" for all claimant countries. In other words, it wouldn't be divided up into sectors the way Old Berlin was before the European Conflict. This proscription remained in effect for almost 20 years.

While the Treaty conditions seemed logical, it soon became apparent that the three-out-of-five voting arrangement would not work. The three native nations, Sioux, Ute, and Pueblo, soon became one voting bloc, and the countries, the U.S. and Aztlan, found themselves with the short end of the stick. After the first

five years, during which the confederation seemed to be guided by a spirit of cooperation, the non-bloc nations finally accepted that they were not wielding any power against the bloc. The U.S. was the first nation to set up its own "autonomous sector" within Denver. The bloc immediately responded by establishing a "native sector," which prompted Aztlan to stake out its own territory. When the Treaty of Richmond was signed in 2034, UCAS used a vague provision in the Treaty of Denver to add CAS to the Denver council by splitting its territories with its new southern neighbor. The decision-making majority shifted to two-thirds (four of six) and eliminated the Pueblo-Sioux-Ute bloc. The nations of the native sector split over what action to take, and in 2035, the native sector fragmented. Pueblo, Sioux, and Ute carved the common native sector into three autonomous sectors.

All six claimant nations recognize that the Council is an ineffective governing body. Unfortunately, the Treaty states that any decision to change the structure of the Council must be unanimous. The Council nations are completely unable to reach a majority decision on any issue of substance, and so it is ludicrous to expect all six to agree on such a significant issue as reorganizing the Council. Since 2031, and for the foreseeable future, Denver's six regions will each be policed by the security forces of one of the Council nations.

The Treaty provision prohibiting countries from levying trade tariffs or taxes on Denver was supposed to prevent any single country from "gouging" the city. The unforeseen result is that Denver has become a free port unlike any other in recent history. While each sector's security contingent will detain and charge traders dealing in contraband that might prove detrimental to its own nation's security, there is no guarantee that the neighboring sectors will feel the same way. For this reason, Denver has become the hub of a well-developed smuggling network. By entering the right sector, smugglers can deal in just about anything virtually under the noses of officials who would be only too happy to break up the trade.

>>>>>[Sound flaky? It is. But it works. I saw a smuggler's panzer running through the Sioux sector with a detachment of Wildcats in hot pursuit; shots fired, the whole trip. The smuggler ducked over into the neighboring Pueblo sector, and the panzer was immediately surrounded by well-armed Pueblo sec forces. The Wildcats were in heavy pursuit mode and either didn't notice or didn't care that they'd crossed the line into Pueblo territory. The Pueblo forces cut loose and geeked every fragging Wildcat. They let the panzer go after they'd established that he wasn't carrying anything that Pueblo considered contraband.]<<<<<
—Miles (07:19:53/3-12-52)

>>>>>[You saw, Miles? I hear you were jamming that t-bird yourself. Loaded to the gills with pirated Cheyenne U tech and you breezed into the wrong sector. But hey, that's just unsubstantiated rumor, right?]<<<<<
—Bung (17:19:39/3-18-52)

>>>>>[T-bird run. Soon. Need riggers and heat. Fax contact information and brag sheet to LTG# 2303 (91-3910). No wimps or tourists.]<<<<<
—Ratchet (20:47:23/3-20-52)

>>>>>[I concur with Miles' observations. I was visiting Denver and was walking through the city center. I turned a corner and saw a group of light LAVs unloading weaponry in an alley. The weapons were still in the manufacturer's original packaging and were mainly assault cannons and miniguns. The area was screened by razorguys armed for war. Anywhere else in the world, my life would have ended there. But in Denver? Two of the samurai approached me and offered me employment.]<<<<<
—Tal Gilgalad (06:49:49/5-20-52)

>>>>>[Did you take it?]<<<<<
—Jeri (16:53:43/5-30-52)

>>>>>[One lead rigger needed, pronto. Must be skilled at no-instrument navigation and have experience in EMCON operations. We'll make it worth your while if you're worth our while. Leave message at LTG# 2303 (16-0382).]<<<<<
—Trisha (14:38:12/5-31-52)

>>>>>[Word to the wise, chummer. Rigging for Trisha is a once-in-a-lifetime experience, if you catch my drift. Ask her what happened to her last lead rigger and whether she sent flowers to his widow. You want a *good* gig, get in touch with me. Relay at LTG# 1303 (35-0040).]<<<<<
—Zak (17:40:17/5-31-52)

>>>>>[I lost my last rigger and his t-bird because someone ratted us to the UCAS hard men. Someone? No, let's be honest here, chummers. Zak ratted us. Ain't that right, Zak?]<<<<<
—Trisha (19:46:30/6-3-52)

>>>>>[Hey—you feel tough, you come talk to me in person. I'll feed your fragging lips to my dachshund.]<<<<<
—Zak (15:41:34/6-6-52)

>>>>>[Children, children. Take your little lover's tiff the frag off my BBS. And the rest of you: this board isn't open to classified ads.

You want riggers or muscle, go recruit somewhere else. Thank you.]<<<<<
—Control (12:55:43/6-9-52)

>>>>>[Let's talk about panzer runs. (No, Cap, this isn't a recruiting pitch. Class is in session.) Denver is the hub of the t-bird run network for a couple of reasons. Sure, it's a free port, but the runs would happen anyway. Denver is in a perfect location: right near the Rockies. That means the t-birds can run right down the mountain range. The perfect tactical situation for a LAV is heavy mountains. (Hold it, you say, that's not what I read in Clausewitz. That's right. I say Clausewitz knew drek about Low Altitude Vehicles. With a few obvious exceptions, the terrain a LAV cruises over doesn't matter: plains, broken ground, mountain valleys, and so on. The only difference is that on the plains a LAV's going to slap a nice big blip on the screen of any sensor array within a couple hundred klicks. In the mountains, there's lots of clutter, even on look-down airborne rigs. You've got to run your t-bird right over the top of ground-sited arrays (or fragging close to it) before they'll know you're there. That's why the Rockies are great: you can play peek-a-boo with the sensors all the way down.) The top-echelon smugglers—not the small-fry who advertise on an open BBS—have their runs marked out and timed. They name their favorites things like Speed Circuit, Route Pack 1, the Ho Chi Minh Trail, and the Autobahn, and they can run them blind at speeds that'll make your sphincters cut loose.]<<<<<
—Hangfire (16:40:48/7-3-52)

>>>>>[Prices in Denver vary, reflecting who's just cruised into town and what they've got in their panzers. Depending on supply and demand, you can pick stuff up for 75 to 150 percent of what you'd pay in Seattle. And if what you're after isn't listed in the Sears catalog, Denver's a great place to get it. Check Tal Gilgalad's entry about the assault cannon. That's not strange, that's business as usual. The "shadow markets" are strong in Denver, and you'll be able to track down just about anything you need. On the other hand, the Better Business Bureau doesn't mean drek in Denver, so tracking the loot down, buying it, and *keeping* it are three totally different things. Lots of dead pigeons in Denver, and I don't mean the ones with wings.]<<<<<
—The Keynesian Kid (13:12:17/7-14-52)

UTE NATION

FACTS AT A GLANCE

Population: 11,658,000

Human:	68%
Elf:	10%
Dwarf:	8%
Ork:	10%
Troll:	3%
Other:	1%

Per Capita Income: 25,500¥
Below Poverty Level: 20%
On Fortune's Active Traders List: 1%
Corporate Affiliation: 16%
Education:
High School Equivalency: 53%
College Equivalency: 27%
Advanced Studies Certificates: 10%
Regional Telecom Grid Access: NA/NAN/UN

CLIMATE

The Ute nation is much of what was once Utah, Nevada, and the southern portion of Idaho. Its climate ranges from semi-arid to temperate mountain forest, with temperatures ranging from well below zero degrees Celsius in the winter in certain regions to the high 30s during mid-summer. In the desert regions southwest of Great Salt Lake, temperatures are even more extreme.

>>>>>[What an understatement. I don't know if it's a result of ozone depletion or what, but the desert has gotten really nasty. Highs during the day often hit 46 degrees Celsius, but it can frost at night. (The temperature can swing a total of 46 degrees or more in 24 hours, which plays merry hell with all kinds of gear, including some cyberware, I'm told.) One garden spot, in what used to be the Dugway Proving Grounds, the Saints call "The Anvil of God." Stories claim that the average daily high there is 48 degrees Celsius. That's the *average;* the high actually runs in the mid-50s. I don't know this from personal experience, but the story's widespread in Salt Lake City.]<<<<<
—Woppler the Weatherman (14:30:44/6-1-52)

>>>>>[Who are the Saints?]<<<<<
—Jersey (12:48:44/7-10-52)

>>>>>[Mormons. "The Church of Jesus Christ and the Latter-Day Saints," or something like that. They still have a hold on Salt Lake City. (Like it says later in the file, if you'd just scan that far, drek-head.)]<<<<<
—Pippin (05:34:39/7-25-52)

>>>>>[If you recall, Dugway was where they tested some of the nastier enhanced radiation weapons—neutron bombs—just before the Chaos…including the ones that didn't work as advertised. I'd be glad to bet a bucket of nuyen that the high temperatures around the Anvil aren't entirely meteorological in origin, if you know what I mean.]<<<<<
—Kit (10:38:24/9-11-52)

ACCESS

Plane

The Ute nation has three major international airports located in Salt Lake City, Las Vegas, and Provo (the capital), and one minor airport in Carson City. The three major ports boast regular service to international airports around the world and have the facilities to accommodate suborbital and semiballistic traffic. Carson City, though strictly international, offers out-of-country service only to nearby major cities, including Sacramento, San Francisco, Portland, and Boise. The Ute nation has a fairly limited internal air transit service. The three major airports are interconnected by a number of short-haul carriers, but connections to other cities and towns are irregular at best and problematical at worst. Those with fixed- or rotary-wing licenses can rent vehicles on a one-way basis.

>>>>>[Rate reductions apply if you're wired with a vehicle control rig.]<<<<<
—Death Jockey (23:10:53/4-29-52)

>>>>>[I had a bad experience with a bird I hired from Air Provo. I lost an entire servo subsystem at an inconvenient moment and came *this close* to flaming in. I've talked to other jet-jocks and they've all had similar experiences or know someone else who's had problems. What I'm saying here is, do your own maintenance check before lifting wheels.]<<<<<
—Peregrin (00:24:20/5-19-52)

Automobile or Bus

The major land routes into the Ute nation are Route 80 heading northeast from Sacramento, Highway 15 leading northeast from Las Vegas, Highway 84 leading southwest from Portland, Route 15 heading south from Butte, Route 70 heading west from Denver, and Route 80 heading west from Cheyenne. All were at one time major interstates and are in fair to very good condition. The Ute nation has no cross-country bus service to speak of. Brigham Young Transit Line, based in Salt Lake City, is the only service in the area. and it serves only a few towns and smaller cities surrounding Salt Lake City. As with most cross-country transit, BYTL buses have video entertainment, though some riders might object to its content.

>>>>>[In other words, it's Mormon religious programming.]<<<<<
—Hacker John (17:26:27/2-1-52)

>>>>>[Don't knock it, chummer. If you don't like it, don't watch, okay? I'm not a Mormon, but anyone who knows them has to admit they're some of the most stable, polite people you'll ever meet—a real shock in a world where stability and politeness are right out of style.]<<<<<
—Mac (23:18:33/2-8-52)

>>>>>[If you're driving into Ute from Pueblo, take my advice and avoid Pueblo Highway 160. It turns into Route 666, the Highway of the Beast (no, I'm *not* kidding), pretty unexpectedly. This highway is not for driving—it's for avoiding at all costs (I'm *not* kidding).]<<<<<
—Bung (04:50:18/8-4-52)

>>>>>[He's *not* kidding. The number dates from way back, pre-90s at least. But the highway has come to earn the number's more sinister denotation. The short stretch between Dove Creek and Monticello, maybe 38 klicks, has more go-gang-related fatalities than *any other stretch of highway* in NA. (Yes, chummers, that includes I-5.) The Highway of the Beast is a round-the-clock battleground. Not for the faint of heart, slow of reaction, or short of ammo.]<<<<<
—Wolverine (20:33:28/8-21-52)

>>>>>[Hey, my kinda highway! Road trip, anyone?]<<<<<
—Midnight Rocker (22:26:21/8-30-52)

>>>>>[It's my sad duty to announce the tragic demise of that drek-headed macho idiot who called himself Midnight Rocker. Don't send flowers.]<<<<<
—Kid Stealth (23:27:18/9-26-52)

TRIBAL DEMOGRAPHICS

The major tribes in the Ute nation are Ute, Comanche, Pawnee, Wichita, Shoshone, Paiute, and Cheyenne. Each tribe's approximate percentage of the population is as follows:

Ute	31%
Comanche	25%
Pawnee	18%
Wichita	10%
Shoshone	6%
Paiute	5%
Cheyenne	5%

The Ute nation was the most thorough of all Native American nations in expelling the white man. This is hardly surprising, considering that Daniel Howling Coyote, leader of the Great Ghost Dance and the war against the United States government, was a Ute. When the Ute territory declared itself as a nation, it issued official edicts that gave non-natives definite, but not unreasonable, timelines for compliance. Unfortunately, one segment of the population felt the time for reason had passed. Bands of native youths prowled the streets of the cities, attacking and frequently killing non-natives who had failed or refused to obey the governmental edicts. Some non-natives fought back in an effort to protect themselves from what were essentially lynch mobs. This only fanned the flames of violence. Small bands became rampaging mobs and occasional casualties became widespread carnage. In downtown Provo alone, official reports claim that over 3,000 non-native residents were killed in a single three-day orgy of violence. (Unofficial reports put the figure much higher.) The mobs made no distinction between the (few) non-natives who were defying the exit order and those who were trying to comply but were unable to do so.

In Tonopah, a mob attacked a convoy of buses carrying non-natives toward California Free State. The militia "security forces" assigned to escort the non-natives on the convoy to the border found themselves in the unenviable position of having to fire on their own countrymen in order to carry out their orders. In other locations, however, militia forces were less conscientious. When a mob attacked a "Relocation Camp" outside Carson City, many of the militia simply stood back and let the mob overrun the camp. Fortunately, however, the majority of the militia believed in their duty to defend the innocent and managed to control the mob before the casualty list grew too long. Despite the militia's efforts, several hundred non-natives died. In an attempt to prevent similar outbreaks of uncontrolled violence, the government brought summary military charges against those militia who abandoned their duty at Carson City. Fifty-seven militia were convicted of desertion of duty and were executed.

>>>>>[Bloody fragging good thing, too.]<<<<<
—Wakeman (09:00:48/8-18-52)

This extreme punishment had the intended effect. The non-native deportation was completed smoothly. Though these events took place decades ago, they are still seriously affecting the nation's fortunes. Ute lacks certain important skill-sets in the high-technology field. The government tried to solve this problem by appealing to immigrants with the appropriate skills, backgrounds, and training. Unfortunately, the majority of candidates with the correct skill-sets were Anglos who remembered or knew of the orgies of anti-Anglo violence the Ute nation suffered. As a result, the Ute nation has utterly failed to attract the immigrants it so desperately needs to regain economic stability.

Those non-natives who live in the Ute nation recognize that only rarely do the old hostilities resurface.

>>>>>[*Official* residents, Danchekker, old boy. Some daring souls live in Ute, particularly in the shadows, whom the government knows drek about. A good number of these are non-native and use magic or tech to disguise their true nature.]<<<<<
—Chrome Rodent (10:14:57/12-13-52)

Non-natives are welcomed by both the government and the populace.

>>>>>[Wrong. The government welcomes them, sure, because they know how desperately the nation needs the immigrants' skills. *Some* of the populace welcomes them for the same reason. But there's still bad blood. Anglos aren't killed outright anymore, but they're sure as hell treated as second-class citizens—or less. If an Anglo's standing in line for something, natives will always butt in front of them. Things will only get tense if you complain. You'll find that restaurants "lose" your reservation and that your confirmed air ticket is now standby if the table or seat is needed by a native. Certain establishments have a strong cultural bias, and patronizing those establishments can be uncomfortable and even downright dangerous. I am one of a group of pinkskins working in the Ute nation who, five years ago, got together and tried to form an official "pinkskin tribe." (After all, we'd chosen the nation as our home, and it wasn't our fault we weren't born Amerind.) After five months of trying to get official sanction, I think we got as far as a meeting with a Second Assistant Back-up Deputy Secretarial Assistant's Assistant Secretarial Assistant or some such drek-head, and we gave up on the whole thing.]<<<<<
—Stacey (22:01:40/1-13-52)

>>>>>[It's gotten better since then, Stacey, believe me. I live in Provo and there are only half-a-dozen places I wouldn't be safe going. I've been here three years and have applied for citizenship. I fully expect to receive it. Sure, the locals are cold until you get past their defenses, but it was as bad or worse when I lived in Puyallup.]<<<<<
—Holmes IV (05:49:02/1-31-52)

The above comments on the Ute policy toward non-natives do not apply to members of the Church of Jesus Christ of Latter-day Saints, the Mormons. The majority of Church members are not native, but they are welcome within the Ute nation. They have their own enclave in Salt Lake City. (The peculiarities of this city are discussed in later sections.) In effect, the Mormons are recognized as a distinct "tribe" and have considerable autonomy in conducting their own affairs. In fact, Ute grants them more autonomy than is given to any other tribal group within the nation. The Utes form the largest proportion of the tribal population and wield an equal amount of political power, but they do not actively discriminate against other tribes.

The elected governmental positions in the Ute nation are filled by members of the majority group, a situation common to democratic governments. Relations between the different tribal groups are cordial. Only one significant complaint has ever been registered. Some twelve years ago, the Cheyenne minority charged the government with maintaining a discriminatory hiring system, but a highly efficient affirmative action program set up by the Elected Council solved the problem. Metahumans are not discriminated against, as long as they have tribal affiliation and descent. (In other words, a metahuman who goblinized from a full-blooded Ute or Comanche, for example, receives the same treatment as ungoblinized tribal members.)

>>>>>[Danchekker's naivete would be touching if it didn't fragging turn my stomach. Metahumans are *always* discriminated against, chummer, no matter what our skin color or heritage. I'm troll. I'm also full-blood Wichita, daughter of a Lesser Chief. I'm 2.7 meters tall, mass around 115 kilograms, and seem to have misplaced my girlish good looks somewhere. I frighten the majority of grown men and all young children. You want me to believe that I'm going to be treated the same as my ungoblinized sister? Get real, Danchekker.]<<<<<
—Native Maiden (15:34:01/8-13-52)

As in the Algonkian-Manitoo Council, certain metahumans in Ute are considering breaking away from their current tribes and forming a new one made up entirely of metahumans. The majority of the metahumans so inclined are elves, though certain dwarfs share this goal. An official proposal to create a tribe to be known as the Wasatch Awakened went before the Ute Elected Council in 2049, but was tabled for further consideration.

>>>>>[Our proposal lingers in bureaucratic limbo, but there are those among us who deny that we even need official sanction. We have acquired land in the Wasatch Forest, and many of us have already taken up residence there in our new homeland. Even if the Wasatch Awakened is never invested *de jure*, it already exists *de facto*, and in our hearts.]<<<<<
—Ellen Spirit Walker (14:10:19/3-4-52)

HISTORY AND CULTURE

The tribes now living in the Ute nation historically come from two distinct regions, the Plains and the California-Intermountain region. Many of the California-Intermountain groups fell on hard times during the mid-1800s, suffering from neglect when the Spanish missions on which they had come to depend were abandoned. These tribes also suffered from war. The Modoc and Nez Perce wars of the 1870s were fierce reactions to the United States government's attempts to move these tribes onto reservations. The Plains Indians, including the Comanche, Pawnee, Wichita, and Cheyenne, also fought long and hard against the incursion of Europeans into their territory.

To battle for their territory was a natural reaction for these tribes because, second to hunting buffalo, warfare was their chief activity. By 1890, however, the buffalo herds had disappeared, along with the Plains way of life. Increasing numbers of Anglo ranchers and settlers moved into the region, and the government moved many Plains tribes onto reservations and encouraged them to take up farming. The warriors of the Plains tribes considered farming woman's work and so turned instead to liquor, warfare, and religious protests. One protest movement was based on the Ghost Dance. The Indians believed that proper, fervent worship would bring back the buffalo and remove the settlers from their land.

>>>>>[Interesting. I thought the Ghost Dance was Zuñi or Hopi or something like that.]<<<<<
—Zack (12:48:12/10-2-52)

>>>>>[You'd know it is if you read my entry in the Pueblo file. But remember, during this period a lot of traditions and mythology passed between tribes. This assimilation often happened through warfare. The crossover of the Ghost Dance was probably a result of Apache and Navaho raids on the Pueblo. They picked up the Ghost Dance with whatever else they took from the Pueblo.]<<<<<
—People Watcher (10:53:29/10-7-52)

The dichotomy between the California-Intermountain and Plains tribes' origins shows in the cultural matrix of the Ute nation. For instance, warfare plays a much smaller part in the Ute, Shoshone, and Paiute cultural traditions. (Some of the California-Intermountain tribes did fight against the United States army, but this was later in their history.) During the earliest part of the European "invasion," Amerindian and Anglo relations relied on cooperation.

>>>>>[Then how come the Ute nation was so keen on booting out Anglos? And so keen on keeping them out?]<<<<<
—Toby (13:36:30/3-10-52)

>>>>>[Check the population balance. The Ute are numerically dominant, but break it down by tribal region—California-Intermountain versus Plains. The C-I tribes represent only 42 percent of the population. And remember that the Ute nation is highly democratic. They were simply outvoted. (Okay, okay, I know that is simplistic. After the re-education camps and the

Resolution Act of 2016, many normally peaceable Amerinds had forgotten about cooperation. But my statement is essentially true.)]<<<<<
—People Watcher (19:40:07/3-10-52)

More members of the California-Intermountain tribes than members of the Plains tribes still affect traditional garb.

>>>>>[Could have something to do with the garb. The C-I tribes typically wore nothing but breechcloths and body paint. Not real practical. Many wear the traditional clothing for ceremonies and the like, though.]<<<<<
—Holly (22:04:58/3-18-52)

>>>>>[The C-I tribes have maintained some traditional art skills. A good example is the basketwork done by the Pomo tribe. (They're less than 1 percent of the population, so Danchekker didn't list them.) Check it out, it'll be well worth your time. It's good work.]<<<<<
—Reba (14:07:27/7-22-52)

The Ute, Paiute, and Shoshone still practice at least one tradition founded in superstition. They hold ceremonies similar to wakes after the death of a friend or loved one and avoid speaking the name of the dead. Superstition holds that speaking the name of a dead person might attract the attention of his or her spirit and call it back to earth.

The Plains tribes, the Comanche, Pawnee, Wichita, and Cheyenne, still reveal remnants of their historically warlike nature. They sparked the violence against Anglos when the Ute nation came into being, and they continue to vote against the easing of immigration laws. Many observers may find the lack of rivalry or friction between the Plains tribes surprising in view of the fact that only 200 years ago they were arch-enemies. The reason lies in their history.

Between the time of the initial Amerindian land claims, in the late 20th century, and the emergence of SAIM and later NAN, many of the Plains tribes united in what was known as the Plains Federation. This organization was basically powerless, but it served as a symbolic rallying point for many Amerindians. In 2011, the Federation dissolved, but it gave an unexpected legacy to the future: the strong traditional rivalry between certain Plains tribes had all but disappeared in the spirit of cooperation.

Among the Plains tribes, ceremonial wear is deerskin breechcloths, leggings, moccasins, and unadorned, natural-fiber shirts. As with other tribes, the majority wear these clothes only on special occasions, though some affect this style of dress at all times.

>>>>>[Even when they're not going traditional, these guys prefer natural fiber clothing to synthetics. That's right, chummers, natural fiber. Believe it or not, it's cheaper than synthetics in Ute. Blows your fragging mind, huh? I'd *kill* for a cotton shirt.]<<<<<
—Seattle Sleuth (14:41:14/2-27-52)

A TRIBE IN PERSPECTIVE: THE CHEYENNE

The Cheyenne were historically the most warlike tribe among the Plains Indians. Originally farmers, they eventually changed their focus to hunting buffalo. They adopted the semi-nomadic lifestyle typical of Plains tribes, traveling and fighting on horseback, living in teepees, and depending on the buffalo for their existence. They warred with other tribes occupying the midwestern United States, especially the Kiowa. The Cheyenne determinedly resisted the incursion of the European settlers and gained a reputation as a proud, fanatically brave tribe.

The Cheyenne suffered greater losses than any other Plains tribe during the ongoing wars against the Europeans. In 1851, the Cheyenne officially split into two subtribes. The southern group lost heart when most of their warriors were massacred by troops at Sand Creek, Colorado, in 1864. The northern branch surrendered to the army soon after the Sitting Bull uprising in 1876.

Demoralized by cholera and defeat, the northern Cheyenne were resettled to a reservation in Montana. They were among the first groups to join the fledgling Sovereign American Indian Movement (SAIM). The southern Cheyenne were relocated to Oklahoma. Though the southern Cheyenne agreed with SAIM's goals, they preferred initially to pursue their land claims through their own organization, the Plains Revival Movement (PRM), an offshoot of the Plains Federation.

In 2012, the PRM officially joined SAIM. Common enemies have traditionally brought otherwise-hostile factions together, but the Cheyenne were unable to forget their hatreds. Serious problems arose again between the Cheyenne and the Kiowa. Perhaps because of Cheyenne influence on the SAIM war council, in the ongoing guerrilla war Kiowa troops suffered casualties totally out of proportion to the tribe's size.

On December 12, 2016, a U.S. Army Ranger battalion received intelligence on a large concentration of Amerindian warriors and materiel located near the battalion's base. In accordance with standing orders, the Rangers pounded the enemy position with artillery and stand-off weaponry to "soften them up." Only when the Rangers ran an assault on the position did they realize their error. The "enemy position" had, in fact, been a refugee settlement housing several thousand noncombatants, mainly women and children, all Kiowa. Investigation proved that the "intelligence" leading to this attack was provided to the Rangers by a group of radical Cheyenne nationalists. For all intents and purposes the Kiowa tribe had ceased to exist.

>>>>>[That's a drek-eating lie, Danchekker! My people would never act so dishonorably.]<<<<<
—Eagle Feather (18:10:02/10-02-52)

>>>>>[They did it, chummer. What price Cheyenne honor, hm?]<<<<<
—Zed (06:12:09/11-10-52)

The Cheyenne have retained the personal code of behavior of their ancestors. Pride is foremost. The majority of Cheyenne will die to avenge a slur against their personal or family honor. Vendetta and revenge are accepted values in the Cheyenne social matrix.

>>>>>[I was talking with a Cheyenne friend about this issue some time ago, and he gave me this example. Say his brother was murdered. In the eyes of his tribe, he would be completely justified in hunting down and killing his brother's murderer. But he would be equally justified in taking no action, because it was his brother's responsibility to see that he didn't get himself killed. Interesting, eh?]<<<<<
—Tapley (11:47:30/3-3-52)

During the Plains Wars in the 18th and 19th centuries, the Cheyenne shared with the Sioux the tradition of "counting coup." This was basically a "body count" of enemies slain or scalped by a warrior. Modern Cheyenne still count coup, but rarely for warfare and the death of their enemies. A Cheyenne may count coup if he defeats a rival in the business arena, at individual sports, or in non-lethal single combat.

>>>>>[Even in war, counting coup did not require killing. Sure, you'd get glory for killing or scalping an enemy brave, but you'd get greater glory for touching a living enemy with a "coup stick" (and living to tell about it, of course). This tradition continues. Cheyenne men will often stop just short of killing an enemy, even when this could later prove dangerous. Presumably this is so the enemy will survive to spread tales of the warrior's prowess. (What it usually means is that the warrior's got a really pissed guy coming at him from the shadows.)]<<<<<
—Holly (10:01:50/4-6-52)

>>>>>[A note on sports. Cheyenne, and I guess Plains Indians in general, are really hot on foot-racing. The whole ritual's invested with this great male, macho, bulldrek aura that makes me want to yarf. And let's not forget that other macho display, "Indian wrestling." I've seen two Cheyenne "braves" Indian-wrestle for almost half an hour before one of them folded. They were so intense on this fragging game that it seemed like a matter of life and death. (And I guess it was. When it was over, the loser pulled a knife and geeked the winner.) Fragging men.]<<<<<
—Bilitis (13:04:40/8-19-52)

The traditional dress of the Cheyenne is common to most Plains tribes: deerskin breechcloths, leggings, moccasins, and simple shirts. In the winter, the costumes include leather robes or cloaks. As with most Amerindian tribes, the majority of Cheyenne wear this traditional garb only during religious ceremonies or on days of remembrance.

>>>>>[You see this kind of traditionalism more frequently among women than men, which has some interesting implications. Men are more likely to dress in traditional clothes when they're discharging a debt of honor such as a vendetta. (So if your Cheyenne buddy who always wears Jedi Kal jeans suddenly appears in breechcloth and leggings—stand aside.)]<<<<<
—Holly (12:23:05/4-6-52)

ECONOMY

The Ute nation operates a basically agrarian economy supported by light manufacturing. The nation also boasts a small but rapidly growing tertiary industry, centered around Brigham Young University (BYU). The nation has strictly enforced, stringent laws concerning waste emissions. In 2048, a Yokogawa subsidiary running a light machining plant in Escalante was fined over three million nuyen for an effluent release into the Escalante River.

>>>>>[You want to hear an ugly fact? The effluent spill that cost Yokogawa 3 mill had at its worst a concentration of nasties less than a fifth of last week's pollutant count off Pier 28 in Seattle. I think I'm living in a toilet and I want to move to Ute.]<<<<<
—Silent Sam (18:41:51/3-20-52)

Manufacturing is generally limited to products used locally. The most notable exception is Facet Visualizations Inc., based in Brigham City. Facet builds simsense components, with a worldwide reputation for excellence.

>>>>>[I have Facet gear, and it's real wiz.]<<<<<
—Static (06:12:43/4-13-52)

>>>>>[It should be, it's got a great pedigree. Facet lifted the design from Hitachi, then poached a hot systems engineer from Toshiba. The CPU's supplied by Sony, who is just jazzed to see somebody walking on Hitachi and Toshiba's market share. When the time's right, anybody want to bet me that Sony won't buy out Facet?]<<<<<
—Nuyen Nick (12:17:03/10-4-52)

Though it cannot boast the high number of fundamental breakthroughs achieved by the University of Cheyenne in the Sioux nation, Brigham Young University has been holding its own in the high technology field. BYU licenses its technology to a local group of small, innovative firms based just outside Provo. It is illegal for any corporation not headquartered in the Ute nation to own more than 3 percent of any company holding a BYU license.

>>>>>[In the industry, we call the licensee companies the "Beltway Bandits" because they're all located in the beltway that rings Provo. Most of them are owned/run by BYU graduates, and most of them are doing very well, thank you. One of them, Stealth Technologies (great name!), markets a real smooth surveillance device that's got corp sec chiefs tearing out their hair. They call it the NFB-100 (which, I hear from a buddy, stands for "Neat Fragging Bug"; I like these guys). What makes it special is that it is invisible to normal bug-sniffers and it's capable somehow of listening right through white noise. Wiz! And it only costs about 5K¥. They can't keep up with demand. (You can be sure that Stealth already has a toy that'll defeat its NFB, and it's only a matter of time before they put it on the market, too.)]<<<<<
—Electron Cowboy (11:38:58/3-3-52)

>>>>>[Newsflash. MCT tried to buy Stealth Technologies. They did it through a front company called Mesotech, but it's an open secret in the shadows that MCT's behind it. The acquisition was disallowed anyway, because the government heard the buzz that MCT was involved. Mesotech's challenging the ruling on the basis that the company actually making the purchase is headquartered in Provo and does no business outside of Ute, and that Mesotech has an arms-length relationship with MCT. (Like drek.) More news when I know it.]<<<<<
—The Keynesian Kid (14:31:05/3-21-52)

>>>>>[Latest word: Mesotech's challenge was thrown out of court! Mesotech's corporate lawyer tried to take it to the Ute Elected Council, but the Council refused to entertain his appeal. (The way I hear it, MCT was sloppy. Word leaked to the Council that Mesotech's fixer had been put on retainer by MCT five years back, and the relationship was never officially dissolved.)]<<<<<
—The Keynesian Kid (12:11:31/9-9-52)

In addition to their research in electronics and software design, Brigham Young University has a worldwide reputation in genetic engineering and chimeric gene-splicing. BYU is responsible for several high-yield strains of grain that grow only in the Ute nation. The strains require no fertilization, little water, and will grow in soil incapable of supporting any other food crop. Several of these strains also yield two crops per year. This allows the Ute nation to grow sufficient grain crops to support its own population, with enough left over to develop a healthy export economy. Other staples are grown hydroponically or in vats.

The majority of the population is vegetarian by choice. What little meat is eaten is imported. In 2032, the Elected Council approved a proposal from Maritech Enterprises of Vancouver (Salish-Shidhe) to convert the Sevier Bridge Reservoir into the world's largest fresh-water fish farm. It was a surprising move in view of the basic insularity and restrictive trade practices of the native nations. The farm proved even more successful than Maritech's glowing projections, and the Ute nation now claims the interesting distinction of being the world's largest trout exporter.

>>>>>[Those Maritech guys are good. They did the fresh-water project in Cultus Lake near Vancouver and a couple of saltwater farms in the Georgia Strait.]<<<<<
—Cap the Knife (11:21:43/2-20-52)

>>>>>[Maybe so, but I smell a rat. Maritech is owned lock, stock, and trout by Aztechnology. We all know how the Big A likes to play political leverage games. And the Sevier Bridge Reservoir project gives it some pretty significant leverage. Aztechnology's got patient money, but sometime soon they're going to make a move. Bet on it.]<<<<<
—Pyramid Watcher (00:27:29/3-3-52)

The standard of living in the Ute nation is high, mainly as a result of its strong high-technology sector and surplus position in grain and other foodstuffs.

>>>>>[And so we play the price differential game again. Baseline Seattle, as always.

UTE COST OF LIVING	
ITEM	**COST**
Weaponry	
Ammunition	100% (1)
Explosives	90% (3)
Firearm Accessories	90% (2)
Firearms	90%
Melee Weapons	100%
Projectile Weapons	100%
Throwing Weapons	90%
Armor	
Armor	110% (4)
Security and Surveillance	
Communications	80%
Security Devices	70%
Surveillance Countermeasures	80%
Surveillance Measures	80%
Survival Gear	100%
Vision Enhancers	90%
Lifestyle	
Lifestyle	110%
Electronics	
Electronics	80%
Cybertech	
Biotech	100%
Bodyware	110%
Cyberdecks	80%
Headware	90% (5)
Internals	90%
Programs	80%
Magical Equipment	
Hermetic Library	120%
Magical Supplies	110%
Magical Weapons	110%
Power Foci	110%
Ritual Sorcery Materials	110%
Spell Foci	110%
Vehicles	
Aircraft	90%
Boats	130% (6)
Ground Vehicles	100%
Military Vehicles	100% (7)

Cost of Living—Notes:
(1) Specialty rounds are kept under strict control of the government. Even security forces from major corps are restricted by the same law: in other words, even MCT's local boys can't use high-carnage rounds. (Legally. As if that stops anyone in the corps.)
(2) Silencers are a no-no, and smartgun rigs and smart goggles are also frowned upon.
(3) Lots of restrictions requiring an (almost) ironclad paper trail. Chemical tracers are put in every lot of locally manufactured explosives, and possession of chem-free blaster is good for a stay in the can.
(4) Armor heavier than lined jackets and the like is restricted, even for corp sec-guards.

(5) Some of the Beltway Bandits dabble in cyber. Their stuff is good and cheap.

(6) Nothing sea-going, only vessels capable of handling large lakes. (Makes sense for a land-locked country.)

(7) This reflects the squeeze necessary to get one from a fixer. All the tech stuff I've listed comes from local manufacturers, mainly the Beltway Bandits. If you've got your heart set on an import, you're going to pay another 50 percent—if you can get it at all.]<<<<<
—The Keynesian Kid (20:59:51/ 2-11-52)

Most of the major multinationals have a presence in the Ute nation. The nation's restrictions on the presence of non-natives restricts the corporations' normal pattern of expansion into a new market, but most of the major players have managed to persuade the government that a few non-native corporate headquarters representatives, mostly at the high executive level, are necessary for the corporation to benefit the country. The vast majority of corporate employees are tribal. Unfortunately for the multinationals, the scarcity of candidates qualified in high technology and big business makes it difficult to find the people they need.

>>>>>[MCT's here, so is Aztechnology, and Yokogawa and Sony have footholds, but they're really hurting without the well-trained corporate sharks they normally employ.]<<<<<
—Dallas (07:18:22/10-13-52)

GOVERNMENT

The Ute nation is governed by an Elected Council of 44 members led by a Great Chief. All positions are filled by election and carry four-year terms. Elections of Council members and the Great Chief are offset by two years to prevent major upheaval. All other positions in government are appointed.

The Ute nation is probably the most truly democratic country in North America. Though the Council and Chief have some discretionary powers, most decisions of the Council must be put to national plebiscite. All elections and plebiscites are conducted electronically. "Polling stations" can be found at virtually every city- or town-core street corner. These stations are simply terminals, industrially hardened to minimize the vandalism, into which voters insert their credsticks as identification. Once the voter is identified, he or she selects the exact election/plebiscite in which he or she is interested (since there

can be and often are several underway simultaneously) and votes using a touchscreen. If the voter has access to a private terminal, voting information can be loaded into the credstick's user-access memory and downloaded instantly upon insertion into the polling station. (This has the advantage of guaranteeing that the voter's selections are secret.)

>>>>>[Turns the whole fragging system into a technocracy, if you ask me. Don't have the tech? Sorry, chummer, you're disenfranchised.]<<<<<
—Retro (06: 07:36/2-16-52)

>>>>>[Drek, boyo. Any citizen with a credstick can vote. The only people who don't have credsticks are lowlife shadowrunners and they don't want our vote anyway, eh?]<<<<<
—Yoshi (05:13:09/3-4-52)

>>>>>[The democracy-for-everything approach seems like a good idea on the surface; very egalitarian, warm, and fuzzy. But frag me if it isn't a nightmare in practice. On any given day, at least two plebiscites are open for voting, more if you include the local stuff with the national. The overhead necessary to handle the whole thing is a fragging pain in the butt and you can be sure it slows down decision-making. Plus, *Vox Populi Vox Dei* usually translates into, "My god, how did we get into this mess?" Remember the definition of an electorate as a creature with a million stomachs and no brain? When I elect someone, I want him or her to make the decisions. Theoretically, the elected official is better trained and better informed about the issues than I am. What the drek do I know about international relations?]<<<<<
—Bennie (23:10:01/5-14-52)

>>>>>[Bennie probably has a point, but the Ute electorate has so far avoided voting themselves bread-and-circuses without regard for the consequences. The system seems to work. And you can't deny that Ute has the best-informed populace of any nation.]<<<<<
—People Watcher (21:05:26/6-7-52)

>>>>>[Here's another problem. Once you've given the "Peepul" something, you can't take it back. The government was given the power to impose "Discretionary Law," under which they may choose not to put everything to plebiscite. It's an emergency measure for critical issues and issues where response time is important. The three times discretionary law was imposed set off unbelievable public outcry, and it was worse each time.]<<<<<
—Detox (14:38:20/6-11-52)

The majority of Council members are shamans. Historically, the Great Chief has also had some shamanic training.

>>>>>[The current Great Chief is a real gem named Margaret Howling Coyote (Daniel's third cousin or something). This is her first term, but she really seems to have her drek together and I'll bet anyone she'll win reelection. Maggie is a Snake shaman, and word on the street is that she's powerful enough to…well, fill in your own overworked analogy. She's Ute, as is about a third of the Council, but this lot really seems to have the best interest of all tribes at heart. Maggie's been trying to open up immigration for non-natives, but her legislation keeps getting killed in plebiscite. She's started a widespread public education campaign to inform the Amerinds that the Ute nation "needs the Anglos, so don't penalize them for their ancestors' actions." It doesn't look like it's working. Her political opponents—particularly a real nasty called Billy Bear (who, despite his name, is Raven totem)—are trying to discredit her by convincing everyone that she's an Anglo lackey.]<<<<<
—Doe (07:05:58/3-12-52)

>>>>>[I agree with Doe. Before Margaret Howling Coyote took office, significant corruption flourished within the government. She immediately took great pains to root it out and destroy it wherever it lurked. She is a wise administrator and a courageous soul.]<<<<<
—Leafsong Gold Eagle (07:57:51/5-12-52)

LAWS

IMMIGRATION

The resistance to non-native immigration enforced by the general populace is notably lacking in the higher echelons of government. Because such decisions must be ratified by plebiscite, however, immigration laws remain rigidly anti-Anglo. Restrictions do not extend to Amerindians from tribes outside the Ute nation, however.

>>>>>[Lie! Navaho are not welcome, and are never accepted for immigration.]<<<<<
—Super Chief (18:47:15/4-13-52)

>>>>>[Don't jump to conclusions. Admittedly, in the past there has been bad blood between the Ute tribe and the Navaho. When the Ute nation was formed, a small but significant population of Navaho lived in the region. The government went to great quasi-legal lengths to relocate them in other nations. Individual Utes and Navaho might not get along, but their differences have settled into the same cool-headed, traditional, ritualistic animosity as is found between the Campbells and MacDonalds in Scotland. The government doesn't condone this prejudice and doesn't practice it.]<<<<<
—Holly (17:35:55/7-17-52)

Non-Ute tribe members are allowed to immigrate freely, but are initially granted only "Resident Alien" status. They may work and maintain permanent residence in the Ute nation, but cannot vote. Only after four years of uninterrupted residence can a Resident Alien apply for citizenship. This rule applies even to members of the nation's major tribes whose official residence is outside the Ute nation.

The government can and does issue work visas to non-tribal people who have skill sets that are in demand, but the application process for such a visa is labyrinthine. Work visas are temporary and must be renewed every two years. The government can cancel them without notice. Citizens of any country may apply for Tourist Visas if they wish to visit the Ute nation. A Tourist Visa is valid for 30 days from date of issuance and can be renewed. Application for renewal must be made from outside the nation, however. A visitor with a Tourist Visa is prohibited from working.

>>>>>[If you're not tribal, this is not a good vacation idea. See some of the earlier comments.]<<<<<
—Holly (17:14:54/12-11-52)

An exception to the general rule on work visas is made for Las Vegas. The employment needs of the city are tremendous, and in order to maintain the steady cash flow that Vegas provides, the Ute have created special channels for Vegas work visas. Applications receive prompt attention and action.

>>>>>[So if you want in, Vegas is the place to be.]<<<<<
—Barracuda (05:21:43/05-15-52)

From time to time, the government also issues Student Visas that allow out-of-country students to attend Brigham Young or any of the nation's other fine universities. As with Tourist Visas, Student Visa applications must be made from outside the country. They are valid for one year from date of issuance, but are canceled immediately when the bearer is no longer a registered student, for any reason. All visas can be revoked without notice by the government. People entering the country under any visa type must carry appropriate documentation with them at all times and should be prepared to show it to any police officer or governmental official who asks to see it. Failure to carry documentation is a misdemeanor, and the visa-holder must present appropriate proof of his or her visa status at the nearest police station or governmental office within six hours of being asked to do so. Residence, even temporary, in the nation without visa or citizenship is a felony crime subject to significant penalties.

>>>>>[If you don't look tribal, the cops will hassle you for no apparent reason. Make sure you carry a visa (or an acceptable forgery) or your life's going to be hell.]<<<<<
—Bonzo (15:11:43/9-18-52)

>>>>>[Amen to that. The Ute border is long and vastly under-patrolled, though recently the Border Force has been buying some wizzer tech from Stealth and the other Beltway Bandits. It's tempting to just fade across the border in the dark of night. But staying inside isn't easy. You've either got to stay deep in the shadows or have good fake paper in your pocket. And that's no guarantee, because some ultra-zealous cops get off on punching visa verification codes into their handy-dandy portable terminals. Your paper might *look* like the real thing, but if the central computer doesn't know about it, you're still in deep drek.]<<<<<
—Hangfire (16:53:37/9-30-57)

>>>>>[Even that problem can be bypassed if you have the nuyen or a good cyberdeck.] <<<<<
—FastJack (03:56:27/11-20-52)

CIVIL AND TRIBAL LAWS

The Ute nation's justice system is based on the Judiciary Council. In Ute, a Council comprises three judges. One of the judges must be a shaman. The two remaining judges are usually shaman, but they are not required to be. Judges must complete five years of extensive ethico-legal training and a very stringent battery of written and oral exams. The basic Judiciary Council trial uses the standard adversarial system with prosecuting and defense attorneys. However, the judges have a great deal of leeway in how they decide to conduct the proceedings. While some judges act as completely objective observers, the majority prefer to take a more active role, acting as "facilitators" in an attempt to reach the truth.

>>>>>[You might be able to find a few bad apples, but most judges are straight arrows. Don't try to bribe them, intimidate them, or shmooze them. They don't appreciate it, and they'll let you know how they feel with a stiff sentence. If you haven't seriously pissed off the judges, you'll find that sentences tend to run about what you'd get in Seattle for the same transgression.]<<<<<
—Legal Beagle (18:00:59/12-25-52)

The Ute nation uses capital punishment, with the sentence carried out by firing squad, often within a week of a conviction. Death row is practically nonexistent. Though the Council has the authority to overturn any conviction or alter any sentence, this authority is discretionary. In other words, there is no recourse to an appeal. If the Council decides a case warrants review, they will do so, but there is no way to request a review of a case. Subtribal groups have their own laws and taboos. These do not carry the weight of national law, and both enforcement and punishment are determined by the groups involved.

>>>>>[The authority of a subtribal group depends on the threat of social sanction.]<<<<<
—Holly (18:17:45/5-16-52)

The only exception to this legal structure is the Mormons, discussed in a later section.

The Ute nation has no distinct armed forces. Law enforcement is carried out by a monolithic paramilitary organization known as the Security Force, which is also responsible for civil defense. Members of the Security Force receive both military and standard law enforcement training and stand ready to respond to whichever force is needed.

>>>>>[In other words, cops are soldiers and soldiers are cops. The SecForce boys are well-trained and well-equipped, with everything you'd expect and more. Regular issue is the lightest armor and a heavy pistol and taser, or maybe an SMG. But they gear up with heavy military weaponry and support equipment when they expect trouble. The ranks are filled with those who couldn't get gainful employment elsewhere, which tells you they're going to have the standard lower-class attitudes—they hate Anglos, is what I'm saying. The Border Force, responsible for immigration, customs, and so on, is a subunit, but people get reassigned on a regular basis. (Which means the street monster who tried to geek you last time you were stirring up trouble in Provo might be at the border the next time you try to enter the nation.)]<<<<<
—Race (23:41:43/1-11-52)

INTERNATIONAL RELATIONS

The Ute nation is on good terms with all other NAN nations and has a strong voice on the Sovereign Council.

>>>>>[You're batting .500, Danchekker. Ute has a strong voice on the Sovereign Council, but it's not on good terms with *every* NAN nation. Can you explain the friction with Pueblo?]<<<<<
—Kiwi (21:54:54/11-21-52)

>>>>>[The history lesson commences. When the NAN was carving up North America, the soon-to-be-Ute nation had its eye on everything straight down to Mexico. That includes the land that's now the Pueblo Council. The Ute claim was based on tribal movements in the early 19th century and other documented evidence. (The fact that the Zuñi and Hopi had been living in the area for several centuries didn't seem to figure into the equation.) When the NAN Sovereign Council ruled that the contested southern section should be given to the Pueblo, relations between the two nations cooled considerably. Decades passed, and some of the more militant of the Plains tribes, mostly Ute, began to once again regret that their ancient homeland was in the hands of cliff-dwellers. In 2038, 2041, and again in 2048, minor border skirmishes flared up between the two nations. Armed groups of Ute residents tried unsuccessfully to cross the border and rip up some Pueblo citizens and property. The Pueblo Corporate Council accepts the Ute Elected Council's claim that these raids were by malcontents, carried out against the official policies of the nation. *But* the Pueblo Corporate Council feels the Ute nation didn't give the problem as much attention as it deserved. The range wars stopped in 2048, but dissatisfaction with the status quo among Ute's disaffected youth might well start them up again.]<<<<<
—Holly (05:58:13/11-29-52)

▼ ▼ ▼ ▼ ▼ ▼

>>>>>[Holly also should have mentioned the "Provo Silicon Party" of 2047. Person or persons unknown broke into a warehouse and dumped a whole shipment of computer equipment imported from Pueblo into the deep end of Utah Lake. It was a trivial incident, but representative of the citizens' general attitude.]<<<<<
        —Watson (16:24:34/12-5-52)

>>>>>[Ute isn't the only place with extremists, you know. A small group of Pueblos think the Ute government was behind the range wars and the "Silicon Party." They believe the raids were just probes testing border security. This group of idiots wants the government to take retaliatory action. At the slightest provocation by the Ute, they'll be pressuring the government to respond in kind.]<<<<<
        —Alter Ego (06:32:38/ 12-7-52)

The Ute nation has cordial, if not particularly warm, relations with both the UCAS and the CAS. Differences of opinion have cropped up over the years, but they have never reached the point where the ambassadors of either side were recalled. The Elected Council is working on building closer trade and technology-exchange ties with Japan. So far, these have met with only moderate success.

>>>>>[What about relations with California Free State?]<<<<<
        —Jocko (06:40:45/2-12-52)

>>>>>[To quote Danchekker, "cordial, if not particularly warm." That might change soon, however. Cal Free is interested in stopping some of the panzer traffic passing through its territory. Since many panzer runs loop through Ute, CFS is currently negotiating to supply Ute with "interdiction measures"—and I have no idea exactly what "measures" they're planning to supply—in return for I don't know what.]<<<<<
        —Jammer (04:47:58/3-6-52)

THE "SAINTS"

When the Ute nation was formed, the Church of Jesus Christ of Latter-day Saints, the Mormons, petitioned the government for special rights as a "distinct society." They requested the right to govern Salt Lake City as a society only nominally part of the nation, analogous to Vatican City in 20th-century Italy, and to dispense justice to their own members as dictated by their religious traditions. The Church had always supported tribal land claims against the United States government. It also represented a significant source of tax revenue which would be lost if it followed through on its implied threat to move to a more accommodating nation if Ute refused their request. The Ute government quickly approved the Mormons' petition.

Salt Lake City is a distinct "enclave" within the greater Ute nation. The Ute's constitution states that Salt Lake City is the same as any other city and under the jurisdiction of the Elected Council; however, the facts are somewhat different. Salt Lake City is governed by a Council of Elders appointed by the Church itself. The Elders are responsible for setting civic policy and for the fiscal management of the city. They always request approval from the Ute Elected Council before enacting any sweeping legislation, and such approval is always given. The Ute Council is little more than a "rubber stamp" where decisions of the Mormon Council are concerned.

Though the Church and inhabitants of Salt Lake City pay taxes to the Ute government, they effectively form a sovereign state within the boundaries of the Ute nation. The exact makeup of the Council of Elders, the selection procedure, and their duties are unknown outside the ranks of the Mormons. The Saints, as many Ute citizens call them, are exceedingly private in conducting their affairs. Presumably, the Ute Elected Council has access to at least some of the details, but these duties are not part of the public record.

Salt Lake City (or "Salt Lake Empire," depending on who you talk to) has no border guards. Everyone is welcome to enter the city, native or Anglo, regardless of religious affiliation. Visitors are free to take up residence and look for work—if they can find it. While there is no official discrimination, it is a fact that very few non-Mormons are employed in Salt Lake City. The faithful evidently prefer to hire from among their own and will select a Mormon candidate over a non-Mormon, assuming both are equally qualified.

Salt Lake City has its own university (also called Brigham Young University, for an important figure in the Mormon religion), which enjoys a good academic reputation. (Most non-Mormons refer to this smaller campus as "Saint U.") In general, the residents of Salt Lake City have a much higher level of education than other residents of the Ute nation.

The Mormons are free to create and enforce their own laws and operate their own police force without interference from the Ute nation. The majority of Mormon laws match those of the rest of the country, with several interesting exceptions. While Ute law mandates monogamy in marriage, the Mormons have returned to earlier traditions allowing polygamies of any size. Laws make public drunkenness, lewdness, and offensive behavior misdemeanors.

>>>>>[More to the point, runners, they have a total ban on all firearms. That's right, a total ban: no hold-outs, no belly guns, no nothing. Even the cops usually pack nothing more lethal than narcojet rifles and tasers. And they don't allow the more lethal types of cyberware, either.]<<<<<
—Zachary (19:02:04/6-3-52)

>>>>>[Then how the frag do they expect to enforce anti-gun laws, hm? Unarmed, unchromed cops…two buddies and I could take over the whole fragging town.]<<<<<
—Crusher (12:00:24/6-15-52)

>>>>>[Don't bet on it. Mormons are basically peaceable types, but they're not stupid. Sure, you and two buddies could geek a bunch of cops. But the survivors would mobilize their Special Response Teams, who are armed to the teeth and fight like angry buzz saws, and they'd hose you for good and all.]<<<<<
—Zachary (16:25:43/6-23-52)

>>>>>[Zack's right. Your typical street cop is a nice, friendly fellow wearing a lined coat and packing something non-lethal—though he's been trained in unarmed combat. But the city Elders realize that not everyone believes in nonviolence. In every quadrant of the city there's at least one Special Response Team. These cadres have been trained by the Wildcats and they can pull some pretty heavy ordnance out of mothballs in a couple of seconds. The Special Response boys are nice, friendly types too…and they'll feel real bad after they've geeked you. Maybe they'll say a few prayers for your soul, or something.]<<<<<
—Hangfire (03:50:10/6-24-52)

>>>>>[It's a weird place. I visited SLC a while back and didn't think twice about the possibility of culture shock. I hadn't made it 10 meters into town before two cops showed up beside me. The first one says—real polite—"Can I do you a service, citizen?" Then he asks me to give up my hunting rifle. And my Ares Predator. And the holdout in my boot (fragged if I know how he knew it was there). When I hesitated, he and his buddy offered—still real polite—to walk me to the outskirts of town. I considered testing out my wired reflexes, but then I looked at the people on the street around me. All Anglos, and all giving me the kind of look I'd give a Sasquatch that wandered into downtown Houston: curiosity, suspicion, a little fear, and a good dose of mild condescension. Rough up a cop in SLC and the whole populace is going to be after you. Not to scrag you. They'll just tell the Special Response Team where you've gone so they can scrag you. I checked my hardware at the door, as the saying goes, and went about my business. Sounds like they ask the same of everyone, including members of the Ute SecForce.]<<<<<
—Bingo (05:33:45/11-9-52)

>>>>>[Here's how they knew you were packing. All the cops carry real sophisticated induction-field metal detectors with directional receptors built into those short silver-tipped swagger sticks they carry. Featuring an FM transmitter and tiny earphones to give the directional squeal, they're real sophisticated and slick. And a little disconcerting until you know the trick.]<<<<<
—Cyberspace Ranger (22:21:19/11-11-52)

>>>>>[And the trick to defeat their trick is to carry only ceramic-body guns like the Gloch 12. Available for the best prices in Ute at LTG# 2801 (30-1038).]<<<<<
—Guns R Us (16:29:16/11-30-52)

The Saints have their own legal system to back up their laws. Bodies of Elders (in this context meaning senior members of the Church, but not necessarily the Council that runs the city) sit in judgment on almost all cases. Again, only Mormons are allowed to attend trials, so little is known about the procedures used. Outsiders who break Mormon laws within the city are usually tried and sentenced by a standard Ute Judiciary Council which holds office within the city.

Mormons rarely commit violent crimes, but those who do are usually turned over to Ute authorities, after first having been banished from the Church. The Elders consider the Ute Judiciary Council a convenience for dealing with outsiders. The fact that they make use of native judges should not be taken to mean that there is any confusion over jurisdiction. Should a criminal from Provo, for example, take refuge in Salt Lake City, the Ute Security Force must provide sufficient evidence of wrongdoing for the city's police force to detain the fugitive.

If the crime for which the fugitive is being sought is not a crime under Mormon law, the police force will make no effort to apprehend the alleged criminal. The decision to hand over the miscreant to the Judiciary Council, however, is made by the Elders and cannot be appealed by Provo. Somewhat surprisingly, this system has worked with few serious problems since the Ute nation was formed.

▼ ▼ ▼ ▼ ▼ ▼ ▼

GENERAL COMMENTS

Some Ute tribes have strong magical traditions, and many of the Council members are shamans, yet the country's government and policies are almost completely free of magical influences. (In other words, there's no organized use of weather magic or other generally beneficial shamanic activities.) The exact opposite is true on the personal level. Shamans are common in the general population and they use their magic whenever the need arises.

>>>>>[The Saints don't like magic, won't practice it, won't teach about it at their university, and don't like anyone using it in Salt Lake City. It's not against the law, but it's certainly frowned upon. Saints won't trust you if you're obviously a magician, hermetic or shamanic, and will refuse to do business with you. (One of them told me that magic is "against the law of God," and that "thou shalt not suffer a witch to live." Go figure.) Shamans and magicians are advised not to display their wares in public in SLC if they want to accomplish anything.]<<<<<
 —Nikky (10:02:30/4-28-52)

>>>>>[On the other hand, the "real" Brigham Young University in Provo has a good Arcane Studies program, and magical illusions are often used as teaching tools in other departments. This is an exceptionally useful technique, particularly in engineering. *Seeing* the stresses in a bridge's structure, thanks to an Entertainment spell, or *feeling* them as if you're *part* of the bridge (with a Stimulation spell), is much more effective than reading about the problem on a screen.]<<<<<
 —Prof (06:17:29/5-27-52)

>>>>>[Let's talk panzer runs, another iffy legal area in SLC. You know that the western areas of Ute are just one big superhighway for illegal panzer operations, particularly those heading for Denver. What you might not know is that a fair whack of panzer trade moves into and out of Ute itself. Obviously, it can't touch good old Denver for convenience. Loading and unloading takes place in the dead of night in the most godforsaken places imaginable. (The Anvil of God—that nasty stretch of desert—is a good choice.) It's interesting to know that the Saints are into free trade and don't give a drek about Ute's import/export laws. As long as you're carrying something they want, but no guns, you can cruise your panzer right into Salt Lake City with no flack. You can sell your load, stock up with cheap tech toys, and hit the road again.]<<<<<
 —Wheels (23:08:35/7-8-52)

>>>>>[It's not that easy. The Saints won't stop you as long as you don't break any of their laws. But the Ute SecForce has a pretty tight sensor screen around SLC. Assuming you rod it into SLC at top speed, you might get past the SecForce. But you can bet your last nuyen that they picked you up, and security will be tighter when it's time to head out again. Smuggling just isn't as easy as it used to be, chummer.]<<<<<
 —Jammer (07:50:38/7-10-52)

>>>>>[Amen to that. I recommend putting everything you can afford into your panzer's electronics suite. The "arms race" is on, and so things get real expensive real fast. Ute has great sensor arrays. No problem, as long as you've got good electronic countermeasures (ECM). Now Ute's installing ECCM along the sensor lines—electronic counter-countermeasures. You turn on your ECM to defeat their sensors. The ECCM picks up your transmission, locks onto your frequency, and burns out your jamming circuits. Of course, ECCM is passive until you start jamming, so you can't pick it up early and knock it out with an ARM or cannon fire. ECCM technology is tricky and doesn't always work, but it's one more thing to worry about in a life already full of worry. Right?]<<<<<
 —Rod Runner (15:10:36/8-15-52)

>>>>>[Just lay a line of cluster bombs down along your course.]<<<<<
 —Mace (15:12:36/8-15-52)

>>>>>[Oh, sure. How have you managed to stay alive so long, Mace, and isn't that solid mass of bone on top of your neck kinda clumsy to carry around all the time? Don't know about you, but I find cluster bomb detonations easier to spot than a low-profile panzer.]<<<<<
 —Rod Runner (15:15:03/8-15-52)

>>>>>Danchekker skipped right over most of the interesting stuff in Las Vegas, so I pulled a section from a rival publication, *SouthWest by Storm*, to fill you in. Enjoy.]<<<<<
 —Barracuda (12:32:08/03-25-52)

LAS VEGAS

True to its century-and-a-half tradition, Las Vegas remains the largest single site dedicated to gambling in the world. (Monaco is second, Atlantic City is third.) Gambling is allowed in other parts of the Ute nation, but under strictly enforced laws. All the laws are thrown away for Vegas. Almost anything goes. Even rigged games are allowed, as long as the "fix" is no more than 1 percent. Interestingly enough, the burden of proof is on the company in charge of the gambling. Without incontrovertible proof that the game is within 1 percent of being fair, the city governor of Las Vegas can revoke a company's license at any time, with no warning.

WEATHER

When you think Vegas, you tend to think hot, arid, and dry, plus every other synonym you can find in the thesaurus. That is no longer the case.

The hottest, driest months have traditionally been June through August, sometimes slipping a bit into September. The temperature ranges, on average, from about 38 degrees Celsius to 25 during the hottest season. As you would expect, the humidity is low, making the heat a little more bearable.

In the last 50 years, Vegas has received increased rainfall July through September. In comparison to the average rainfall in cities like Seattle, Vegas rainfall is more like a prolonged drizzle, but even rainfall of less than 30cm, distributed over the entire year, is enough to foul up traffic.

>>>>>[That's no joke. Water hits the pavement and every wheel jockey in Vegas forgets how to drive.]<<<<<
—Nik Tap-Dancer (23:18:52/05-15-52)

>>>>>[That may be true, but it really does flood when it rains. For nearly a century, the intersection of Charleston and I-15 has flooded out completely at the lightest rainfall. Since the Awakening, locals (and city officials) have been blaming a Spirit.]<<<<<
—Barracuda (06:42:31/06-03-52)

>>>>>[If it's a spirit, it's the spirit of a 20th-century engineer. These guys must have skipped Drainage 101 in school, because they sure didn't think it was important to put it in the city plans.]<<<<<
—History Buff (10:27:06/06-04-52)

>>>>>[Don't forget the natural washes that have shown up along Boulder Highway heading out of town, just past the Sahara.]<<<<<
—Wiped Out (13:07:55/06-05-52)

Snowfall during the winter months has also increased dramatically. The temperature should not fall low enough in this area to support snow, but in recent years fairly regular temperature drops have made snowfall common. The quirk blizzard of '39 almost froze the city solid.

GETTING IN

Las Vegas is served primarily by McCarren International Airport, located to the south of the city proper. The expansion of 2036 gave the multi-runway facility domestic, international, trans, and suborbital capability. Regularly scheduled transcontinental flights are available to accommodate the international character of the city.

>>>>>[Security at McCarren is pretty severe, generally speaking. The field serves a number of private carriers arriving from points around the world, and the metro police are very serious about insuring their cargoes' safety.]<<<<<
—Shouts At Stars (02:18:12/05-25-52)

Air access to the city is also available through either Sky Harbor Airport in Henderson or further southeast at Boulder City Airport.

Principle road access is I-15, which runs down toward Baker, CFS, and Highway 95, and is roughly north and south.

High-speed rail links run between Vegas and Los Angeles and Vegas and Denver.

GETTING AROUND

Most Las Vegas citizens use their own cars and motorcycles for transportation. Visitors often make their hotel their base and use either the fairly extensive bus and taxi system or the elevated rail system to get around on the strip. Vehicle rental is readily available to travelers wishing to tour the surrounding countryside.

Many of the hotels and resorts provide shuttle-bus transport for guests. Those who can afford it can hire local rotorcraft services.

THE REGION

Within the city, the most frequented area is the internationally famous Las Vegas Strip. Nearly three kilometers long, the Strip is lined on both sides by enormous hotels, casinos, and resorts catering to every imaginable need and desire. Most are independently owned, but some are owned by small business syndicates that quietly control multiple sites. The city has numerous control and ownership regulations and has been fairly strict in their enforcement.

Another major entertainment area downtown is Freemont Street. Offering attractions similar to the Strip, Freemont features the remnants of Vegas' original entertainment explosion. Though the sites are older, they remain popular, especially with the locals.

A third entertainment area has opened up near the McCarren expansion. A handful of hotels and resorts in the area caters primarily to big-ticket events and their patrons. The area's nickname, Twilight, refers to the fact that most of the area's events are scheduled to begin after the sun sets. One of the main attractions is the fabled Tark Dome, the second-largest enclosed stadium in the world.

The neighborhoods of the west and southwest sides are primarily residential, home to many of those who work in the big resorts and casinos. The northwest side has seen better days, but is part of a recent city-funded rehabilitation that is bringing new life to the area.

>>>>>[Notice that North Las Vegas isn't mentioned here? Just wait till they talk about crime.]<<<<<
—Shanty Man (09:16:49/06-19-52)

South of Vegas is the industrial area of Henderson, and to the southeast, Boulder City, a residential-commercial area.

>>>>>[Boulder City was built specifically to house the workers who built the Boulder/Hoover Dam that created nearby Lake Mead.]<<<<<
—Barracuda (14:03:19/03-25-52)

GOVERNMENT

Las Vegas is run by a city governor and a City Council, appointed by the government in Provo. Police and security services are provided by the Las Vegas Metropolitan Police. Las Vegas has five Judiciary Councils, at least one of which is open for business any time of the day or night.

>>>>>[If you walk the strip, you'll see that the MetroPol boys are routinely more heavily armed and armored than forces elsewhere in Ute. When things get heavy, they gear up like army shock-troops.]<<<<<
—Hangfire (23:18:04/3-29-52)

>>>>>["Vegas is run by a city governor appointed by the government in Provo." Drek! Vegas is run by a lackey of the Mafia, and they have a death grip on every gambling concern in the city. The rubber stamp on the governor's letter of office might come from Provo, but the real authority is much closer to home.]<<<<<
—Chie (11:06:54/3-30-52)

>>>>>[Don't be too sure of that. Two months back, Governor Mabel Fox (god, what an armor-plated thorough-going bat) ordered a heat wave against some Mafia operations that were getting too heavy-handed. They picked up a couple of mob chieftains and a whole drek-load of Mafia soldiers got themselves geeked. Two weeks later, a Mafia death squad came within a hair of geeking Fox in retaliation. Now the war is really on. Doesn't sound to me like the governor's bought and paid for by the mob…]<<<<<
—Wiseguy (23:11:09/4-5-52)

Law enforcement is as good as elsewhere in the Ute nation, but tends to be stricter in the high-income and high-tourism areas. As one might expect, enforcement is not as heavy in less-well-traveled areas like North Las Vegas.

CRIME

Speaking frankly, a visitor to Las Vegas will only find danger if he or she wanders away from the main entertainment areas. North Las Vegas has been torn apart by gang problems since the turn of the century when the malcontents emigrated from Los Angeles. Shortly after the Treaty of Denver was created, many of the gangs began to exploit Vegas' convenient geographic location as a stop-over and distribution point for smuggling runs into and out of the Native American Nations. These days, the gangs seem to be dominated by anarchists of all races and creeds who display an alarmingly keen business sense.

ARTS AND ENTERTAINMENT

It has been said that any form of entertainment can be found in Las Vegas…for a price. It is impossible to support or deny that claim here. It is true, however, that Las Vegas has a range of betting games of unparalleled width and depth. Gamblers can bet on dice, wheels, cards, horses, gladiatorial games—the list goes on.

>>>>>[They aren't kidding about gladiatorial games. "The Pit" is open 24 hours a day and you can watch warriors going at it with swords, net and trident, knives, chains, and just about every other weapon known to man (and some that aren't). Most bouts stop at first blood, but occasionally, fights go to the death.]<<<<<
    —Caligula (10:15:34/2-10-52)

>>>>>[Caligula is correct. I went to the pit last week, simply to see for myself if what I had heard was true. I was unlucky enough to see a fight to the death. The combatants fought with knives and lengths of chain. The warriors were strong, fast, and evenly matched, and the bout lasted several minutes. One warrior fell when a swung chain smashed his knee. He tried to hamstring his opponent with his knife, but another slash with the chain shattered his hand and disarmed him. The winner turned to the crowd for their decision. Everyone made a thumbs-up or thumbs-down gesture. The majority voted thumbs-down—so the victor slew the other warrior with his knife, while the crowd howled their approval. I left and was physically, violently ill.]<<<<<
    —Tal Gilgalad (21:20:38/3-9-52)

>>>>>[Tal, old chummer, I have good news for you. Those bouts are faked. (I should know, I consulted for the company that puts them on.) What you saw was very effective theater. Nobody gets hurt (much), and nobody dies. But it sure looks real, right?]<<<<<
    —Hulk (22:11:43/3-9-52)

>>>>>[The reigning champion in the gladiator pit looks exactly like a young Senator Schwarzenegger (remember him, from about 50 years back?). I don't know if it's cosmetic surgery or just a fluke. But the guy acknowledges the similarity: he fights under the name of "Conan the Republican."]<<<<<
    —Bladerunner (02:54:24/3-10-52)

>>>>>[The Vegas mafia have imported something special from Russia: pistol games. You know the kind. Two "players" sit across the table from each other. On the table between them is a revolver loaded with one bullet. They take turns putting the pistol to their head and pulling the trigger. The crowd bets on who blows his brains out first. It's one of the biggest draws in town.]<<<<<
    —Mel (11:27:15/3-16-52)

>>>>>[And, like the gladiator games, it's all faked. (My work again.) It's done just like in the old movies: blanks, blood packs, and squibs. Even if you know it's faked, it looks plenty real enough to twist you up.]<<<<<
    —Hulk (19:47:01/3-17-52)

>>>>>[Not all of it's faked, chummer. I know for a fact that some private clubs for high-rollers make the games real. (The participants don't know that, of course—they think it's another one of Hulk's F/X extravaganzas.) Sick-o.]<<<<<
    —Bit Basher (00:33:16/3-18-52)

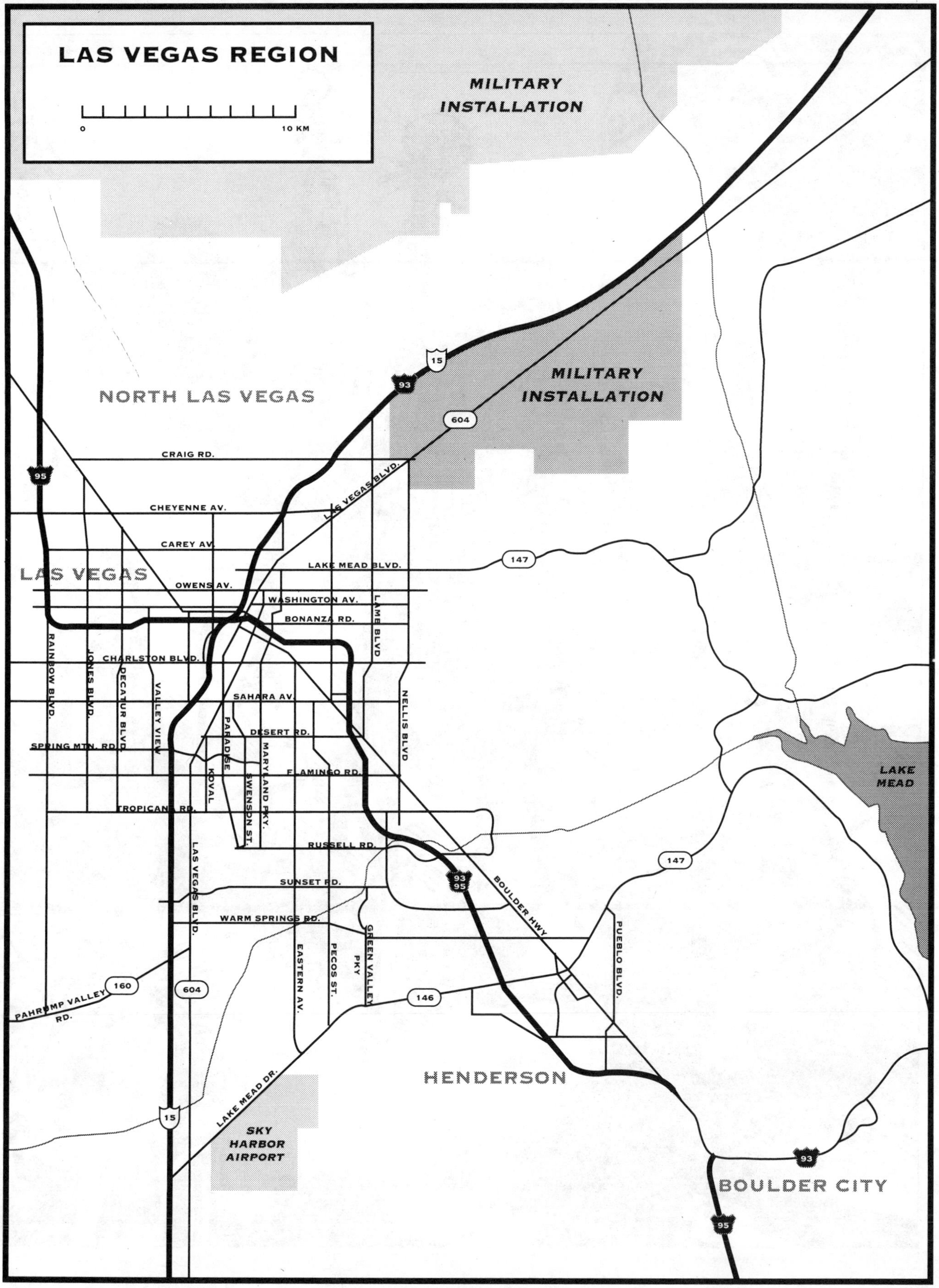

LAS VEGAS REGION

0   10 KM

MILITARY INSTALLATION

MILITARY INSTALLATION

NORTH LAS VEGAS

LAS VEGAS

CRAIG RD.

CHEYENNE AV.

CAREY AV.

LAKE MEAD BLVD.

OWENS AV.

WASHINGTON AV.

BONANZA RD.

CHARLSTON BLVD.

SAHARA AV.

DESERT RD.

FLAMINGO RD.

TROPICANA RD.

RUSSELL RD.

SUNSET RD.

WARM SPRINGS RD.

RAINBOW BLVD.

JONES BLVD.

DECATUR BLVD.

VALLEY VIEW

SPRING MTN. RD.

LAS VEGAS BLVD.

PARADISE

KOVAL

MARYLAND PKY.

SWENSON ST.

NELLIS BLVD.

LAME BLVD.

LAS VEGAS BLVD.

EASTERN AV.

PECOS ST.

GREEN VALLEY PKY.

PUEBLO BLVD.

BOULDER HWY.

PAHRUMP VALLEY RD.

LAKE MEAD DR.

SKY HARBOR AIRPORT

HENDERSON

LAKE MEAD

BOULDER CITY